Instructor's Guide for *Lives in Progress*

Paul H. Brookes Publishing Co.
Post Office Box 10624
Baltimore, Maryland 21285-0624

www.brookespublishing.com

Typeset by Barton Matheson Willse and Worthington, Baltimore, Maryland.
Manufactured in the United States of America by
Pavsner Press, Baltimore, Maryland.

The case stories in this book are based on actual experiences of professionals working in early intervention. Names, places, and certain aspects of the situations have been altered to mask the true identities of those whose lives are described. In some instances, the cases are composites of numerous real-life situations.

An accompanying text, *Lives in Progress: Case Stories in Early Intervention,* can be purchased separately. To order, contact Paul H. Brookes Publishing Co., P.O. Box 10624, Baltimore, Maryland, 21285-0624 (1-800-638-3775; www.brookespublishing.com).

The matrix on pages iv and v was developed with assistance from Sherra Vance.

ISBN 1-55766-373-4

Instructor's Guide for *Lives in Progress*

by

P.J. McWilliam, Ph.D.
Frank Porter Graham Child Development Center
University of North Carolina at Chapel Hill

·P·A·U·L·H·
BROOKES
PUBLISHING Co

Baltimore • London • Toronto • Sydney

Story	Age of child (in years)	Autism	Behavior problems	Hearing impairment	HIV/AIDS	Medically fragile	Mental retardation	Multiple and severe disabilities	Prader-Willi syndrome	Premature birth	Speech-language delays	Vision impairment	Extended families	Low-income families	Middle- to upper-income families	Siblings	Single parenting	Teenage parenting	Child abuse and neglect	Conflicts within families	Domestic violence	Emotional situations	Institutionalization	Sexual abuse	Substance abuse	Child care quality	Communicating with families
Heaven's Glory	0–3							✓															✓				
La Maestra	0–3			✓									✓		✓							✓					
cc: Parker Ellis	3–5		✓				✓							✓													
An Uncertain Future	0–3					✓					✓	✓														✓	
Happy Birthday!	3–5		✓														✓										
Recipe for Rachel	3–5								✓																	✓	
Silent Partner	3–5										✓			✓													
Grandpa's Lap	3–5							✓					✓	✓											✓		
A Family Feud	3–5												✓			✓				✓					✓		
Sunset View	0–3	✓												✓							✓						
Daria's Silence	0–3				✓	✓							✓			✓	✓							✓			
The Need to Know	0–3				✓									✓		✓	✓					✓					
Beyond Duty	3–5																										
Proceed with Caution	3–5																				✓						
Passing Time	0–3								✓				✓			✓	✓		✓								
Absent Mother	0–3												✓	✓		✓	✓		✓					✓			
Mother of Two	0–3													✓	✓	✓	✓						✓				
Money Matters	3–5							✓						✓	✓												
A Change of Plans	3–5										✓		✓									✓					
Leaving Wisconsin	3–5																										

Matrix table. Row titles listed vertically at left; column categories listed at bottom. Checkmarks (✓) indicate intersections.

Professional issues (continued) — columns: Community resources, Confidentiality, Consultation, Cultural diversity, Developmental therapies, Family-centered practices, Initial home visits, Integrated therapies, Interagency coordination, Interdisciplinary coordination, Interprofessional conflicts, Intervention planning, Parent–professional conflicts, Personal safety, Professional boundaries, Referrals, Service coordination, Specialized therapies, Supervision, Teaming

Aspects of service delivery — columns: Assessment and diagnosis, Classroom or center-based services, Clinic-based services, Family support services, Home-based services, IEP, IFSP, Inclusion, Transitions

	Comm. resources	Confidentiality	Consultation	Cultural diversity	Developmental therapies	Family-centered practices	Initial home visits	Integrated therapies	Interagency coord.	Interdisc. coord.	Interprof. conflicts	Intervention planning	Parent–prof. conflicts	Personal safety	Prof. boundaries	Referrals	Service coord.	Specialized therapies	Supervision	Teaming	Assessment & diagnosis	Classroom/center-based	Clinic-based services	Family support services	Home-based services	IEP	IFSP	Inclusion	Transitions
Heaven's Glory						✓				✓				✓										✓	✓				
La Maestra				✓					✓						✓	✓								✓	✓				
cc: Parker Ellis											✓							✓										✓	✓
An Uncertain Future							✓		✓	✓					✓						✓				✓				
Happy Birthday!			✓														✓								✓			✓	✓
Recipe for Rachel						✓					✓	✓	✓						✓	✓			✓					✓	
Silent Partner													✓										✓						
Grandpa's Lap				✓				✓		✓		✓	✓					✓								✓	✓		
A Family Feud			✓	✓																		✓						✓	
Sunset View		✓											✓	✓							✓			✓					
Daria's Silence		✓		✓																	✓		✓	✓	✓				
The Need to Know		✓												✓							✓			✓					
Beyond Duty		✓	✓											✓							✓								✓
Proceed with Caution			✓	✓			✓														✓				✓				
Passing Time													✓																
Absent Mother								✓					✓												✓				
Mother of Two		✓											✓			✓								✓	✓	✓			
Money Matters	✓					✓		✓				✓												✓	✓				
A Change of Plans					✓																	✓						✓	
Leaving Wisconsin						✓					✓	✓							✓	✓	✓					✓	✓		

Contents

Introduction

The case method of instruction (CMI) differs significantly from more traditional methods of teaching. Consequently, instructors who are using this approach for the first time may feel awkward and unsure of themselves. General tips for conducting case discussions are reviewed in this introduction; however, the primary purpose of this manual is to provide preservice and inservice instructors with specific suggestions for using the case stories that appear in ***Lives in Progress: Case Stories in Early Intervention.*** Although none of the materials in this manual are intended to be used as step-by-step procedures, I hope that these guidelines will provide some helpful ideas for instructors to incorporate into their own teaching through the case method.

Orientation to the Teaching Notes

I have provided teaching notes for each case story that appears in ***Lives In Progress: Case Stories in Early Intervention*** in the same order that the cases appear in the main text. I have also included supplemental case materials and suggested teaching activities for a few of the stories in order to expand the story's use to accomplish special teaching objectives. Each set of teaching notes is composed of

- A list of *topics* that the case story addresses
- A brief *synopsis* of the story itself
- The *major issues* that are likely to arise in class discussion
- *Teaching notes* to guide you in facilitating the case discussion

I have designed the first three items to help you select a case story that is appropriate for use with your particular audience and that will accomplish your predetermined teaching objectives.

The list of *topics* provides a quick content outline that may be consulted when searching for an appropriate case (e.g., intervention planning, parent–professional conflicts, assessment, child neglect and abuse). The matrix on pages iv–v provides a summary of the relevant topics for each case story. Several factual parameters of the story (e.g., age of child, home-based services, urban setting) are also included in the list. The topics are listed in descending order of their importance to the story, with the most prominent issues appearing in boldface print. The list of topics, however, is in no way exhaustive. Some instructors may find a case story useful for teaching content or skills that I had not envisioned as pertinent to the case when I developed the case and the teaching notes.

The *synopsis* describes the primary characters in the case and provides a brief overview of the story's events and the circumstances surrounding the events. Together, the list of topics and the synopsis should provide sufficient information for you to determine whether a particular case story is an appropriate match for your teaching objectives and your intended audience.

Finally, the section describing the *major issues* addressed by the case story provides additional information to help you determine whether the story is appropriate for your intended use. Before a final decision is reached, however, you should read the actual case story to ensure that it will suit your purpose.

The *teaching notes* provide you with specific strategies for facilitating the discussion of each case story. I have included examples of leading questions for opening various topics or phases of the discussion, follow-up questions for facilitating more in-depth discussion of particularly important or controversial issues, and suggestions for how to make the transition from one issue to the next. In most instances, the sequence of topics and questions outlined in the teaching notes closely conforms to the steps in the decision-making process that are described in the next section. It is not my intention, however, that you should attempt to follow the teaching notes to the letter. In fact, doing so would, in all likelihood, result in violating important premises of the case method.

Each audience's approach to a case will be unique, affected by the experiences, knowledge, and personal biases of each participant. It is extremely important for you to understand the issues with which a particular group is grappling and to be responsive to the group's unique learning needs. Trying to force the group into following a preset agenda for discussing the case will be counterproductive. Instead, you must be flexible, listening carefully to what participants are saying, following their leads whenever possible, and tailoring the discussion to fit the group's unique needs. Being flexible does not mean that you should relinquish all control over the discussion's direction. You should, however, continuously monitor the discussion and be willing to adjust your original teaching plans as the discussion proceeds. For example, rather than force the group to go through the decision-making process in a rigid, step-by-step fashion, you may decide to allow the group to bypass a step or two if the discussion is "hot." At a later point, you can gently redirect the discussion back to the neglected steps. It is rare, in fact, to have a case discussion in which the decision-making process is strictly followed. Discussions typically go back and forth many times among the various steps in the process. The important thing is for you to be constantly aware of your original teaching objectives and to redirect the discussion at appropriate times in order to accomplish those objectives.

The Decision-Making Process

The decision-making or problem-solving process that should be followed while conducting case discussions varies among different sources. Most sources, however, include the steps outlined in Figure 1. Pat Snyder and I developed this particular version of the decision-making process several years ago to describe the steps we follow while conducting our own case method teaching with early interventionists. A brief description of the questions to be answered during each step of the decision-making process is provided in the remainder of this section.

Identify Problem(s)   What has gone wrong in the situation? With which issues are the various characters in the case story struggling? What can be done to improve their situation?

Identify Positive Aspects   Although identifying positive aspects of the situation is not typically included in other renditions of the problem-solving or decision-making process, it is included in Pat Snyder's and my model to guard against the propensity for students to be overly critical. The question to be answered in this phase is what, if anything, has gone *right* in the situation so far? Has the service provider(s) featured in the case story done anything of which participants approve? In some cases, it may also be appropriate to ask about any positive attributes displayed by other characters in the story (e.g., family members).

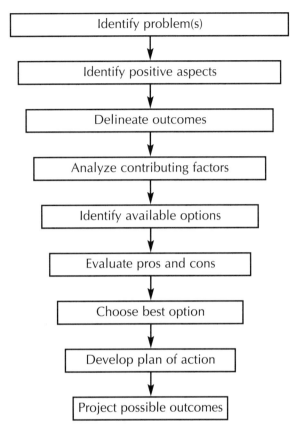

Figure 1. The decision-making process. (*Source:* McWilliam & Snyder [1993].)

Delineate Outcomes   What is hoped to be achieved by solving the dilemma? What would be the ideal outcome and what would be an acceptable outcome? Oftentimes this stage of the process is discussed in conjunction with identification of the problem; however, sometimes it is helpful to distinguish the current problem(s) in the situation from what the situation might look like if it were resolved successfully. Desired outcomes may include additional services that will be provided to the child and the family and how they will be delivered, positive developmental outcomes for the child, improved quality of relationships among various characters in the situation, and a change in the types of feelings experienced by the family members or the professionals.

Analyze Contributing Factors   How did this problem arise? What may have contributed to the problem? Answering these questions requires the participants to analyze the actions (or inaction) of the various characters in the story, the possible motives behind the characters' behaviors, and the circumstances surrounding the situation (e.g., political factors, resources available in the community, the structure of services).

Identify Available Options   What could the service provider(s) featured in the story do to repair the damage or to improve the situation? Without changing the circumstances in the story, what options are available? Depending on the particular case being discussed, it may be necessary to identify both short-term and long-term solutions. A specific case may also require participants to identify solutions for more than one problem. It is extremely important that several alternative solutions be generated for each problem addressed in this phase of the discussion.

Evaluate Pros and Cons   Of all the options suggested for handling this situation, which has the highest likelihood of producing the desired results? What are the pros and cons of each option?

Choose Best Option   Given the pros and cons of each option, which option should be implemented in this situation? Why?

Develop a Plan of Action   If the chosen solution were actually implemented, what actions would the service provider(s) take tomorrow? Next week? Over the next 3 months? The next 6 months? This stage of the decision-making process entails planning the chosen solution. For some cases, this may involve identifying resources that are needed to implement the solution and deciding how the service provider(s) might go about securing these resources. For other cases, participants may be asked to determine the exact words that a service provider should use in a conversation with the parent in the story or with a professional from another agency.

Project Possible Outcomes   Although participants selected the preferred solution largely on the basis of its ability to produce the desired outcome(s), there may be unanticipated effects. What might these effects be? How might the various characters in the story react when the plan of action is implemented? What should the service provider do if the chosen solution does not work as planned?

In reviewing the process outlined previously, it is immediately obvious that there may be considerable overlap among the steps in conducting a case discussion. This is expected and should not be considered a problem. It is perfectly okay to let the participants jump from one step in the process to another; trying too hard to prevent this would be very disruptive to the flow of the discussion. Nevertheless, you should always keep the decision-making process in mind and use well-placed questions to re-direct the group back to neglected steps. Furthermore, it is important to realize that not every case discussion has to be carried through to a complete resolution, for it is the *process* of arriving at a solution rather than the solution itself that is of primary benefit to trainees.

Environmental Arrangements

CMI can be implemented in almost any preservice or inservice environment; however, the instructor's job is much easier if the environmental conditions are conducive to the method. Environmental arrangements should promote ease of conversation between the instructor and the participants and among the participants themselves. A well-lit room is important to allow participants to see one another and stay energized. Seating should be arranged so that participants are close to one another and are facing the other participants in the room. A circular arrangement of chairs, a conference table, or a U-shaped arrangement works well. Although some participants are not bothered by the absence of tables, a few may find it disconcerting; therefore, it would probably be best to keep tables in the room. Most instructors prefer to remain standing in order to write on the board or on flipcharts and to circulate around the room during the discussion. Even so, the instructor's position should not be too far removed from the rest of the group (i.e., not on a raised platform or behind a desk or podium). In general, the more informal the room arrangement, the more conducive it will be to conversation. Typical classroom environments can usually be adapted easily for use by rearranging the furniture before instruction begins.

It is important for the instructor to have an ample amount of writing space in the room. Regular classroom boards (chalkboards or dry erase boards with markers) are preferred; however, flipcharts are a satisfactory alternative if more than one flipchart is used or if the instructor can tape completed papers to the wall so that participants can refer easily to earlier notes. (*Note:* Flipchart paper is now available that will stick to the wall without the use of additional adhesives.) An overhead projector should be used only as a last resort, as it usually requires darkening of the room and the amount of space available for writing is extremely limited.

Above all else, excellent classroom acoustics are essential to the case discussion environment. It is extremely important for participants to be able to hear the instructor and one another clearly without the use of any type of amplification. Acoustics typically are not a problem in university classrooms or other educational facilities, but they can be disastrous in various inservice training locations. Hotel conference rooms, where acoustic tiles and carpeted walls are specifically designed to soak up sounds, are among the worst environments for training. If possible, you should check on room acoustics ahead of time or convey the importance of proper acoustics to the inservice host.

Preparing for Discussion

Just because you cannot predict the exact direction that a case discussion will take doesn't mean that you shouldn't prepare for it. On the contrary, preparation is crucial to the success of the method. First, **know the case material** well. Even if you have used the same case story many times before, *always* take the time to read it the day before or the day of the discussion. When using a new case story, you may want to read it several times to ensure that you are familiar with every detail of the case. Participants may neglect important information, make unwarranted assumptions about the characters or the events that take place in the story, or remember facts incorrectly. It is your responsibility as the instructor to correct the participants if such issues arise. The last thing you want to do is fumble through the pages of the case in search of information during the actual case discussion.

Second, **know your teaching objectives,** and determine which issues in the story should be addressed to accomplish your objectives. You may want to write your objectives on a piece of paper or on an index card. The notes are just for you, so they need not be elaborate, detailed, or even written in complete sentences. Simply jot down what it is that you hope participants will have learned by the conclusion of the case discussion. If some objectives are more important than others, put a star or an asterisk beside these items. Then, on a separate sheet of paper or an index card, write down the aspects of the case story that are most relevant to your objectives or make a short list of leading questions you can ask to open up discussion of these major issues. You may want to consult the teaching notes and the discussion questions found at the end of each case story for ideas. You can use these notes during the discussion, but be careful not to rely on them too heavily. It's not a good idea to let your audience think that you have a preconceived agenda. Therefore, keep your notes to a minimum, and try to use them inconspicuously. Thus prepared, if the discussion starts to ramble and you're not sure where to go next, you can refer to your notes and get the discussion back on track.

Finally, you should **be knowledgeable about the topics or content areas** addressed in the case stories that you use in the classroom. For example, *Recipe for Rachel* is about a child with Prader-Willi syndrome. Before discussing this case, you should ensure that you are well-versed in the symptoms and treatment of Prader-Willi syndrome. This does not mean that you need to be an expert on every topic covered in the cases you use, but you should have at least enough knowledge to be able to answer participants' questions when they arise. It is wise to remember that trainees cannot apply what they don't know. Because of this, you may need to provide factual or theoretical knowledge to participants before starting a case discussion or in the midst of the discussion itself. In case method circles, we refer to the latter as a *mini-lecture.*

Preparing Participants for Discussion

It is also the instructor's responsibility to take whatever measures he or she can to ensure that participants are prepared to participate in the case discussion. If this is an audience's first experience with the case method, you will probably want to provide them with a brief overview of the method, including its purposes and what participants can expect during the discussion. The introduction to the main text, ***Lives in Progress: Case Stories in Early Intervention,*** provides a summary of this information. You can assign this summary as a preclass reading for preservice audiences, but you still may wish to talk directly with students about the information in class. Inservice audiences are less likely to read such information, even if participants receive the materials prior to the class, so you should take a few minutes to review the case method with them before discussion begins.

Most important, you will want to ensure that all participants have read the actual case story prior to the discussion. This is fairly easy with preservice audiences, as you will usually have ample contact with them during which you can convey the importance of reading the case prior to class. You may also choose to have preservice students write out answers to selected discussion questions and turn in this assignment at the beginning of class. Assigning reading to inservice audiences may be slightly more difficult. In some cases, you may not even know who is going to be in the audience prior to the actual training event. Under these circumstances, you may decide to have participants read the case materials during the training event. One solution might be to extend the lunch break an extra 20–30 minutes to provide reading time; however, if you choose this solution, you should consider having participants read the case *before* going to lunch rather than when they get back! If your training spans more than 1 day, you can designate overnight reading assignments. You might also consider giving participants the option of reading the case the following morning during a half-hour period before the actual training begins. If you do this, it's nice to make refreshments available during this reading time.

Tips for Facilitating the Discussion

This section contains general tips that you should keep in mind while facilitating a case discussion. Some of these ideas come from my own experiences with the case method, but many of these tips represent the accumulated and shared wisdom of numerous case method instructors working in a wide variety of professional disciplines over the past half century.

Use Questions to Guide the Discussion   Questioning is the primary method you should employ to guide the case discussion. The purpose of questioning is not to "test" the participants, stymie them, or to probe for the "right" answer. Instead, questions should be thought-provoking: They should encourage participants to look at situations from new angles and to question the reasoning behind their opinions and answers. Therefore, open-ended questions are preferable to those that limit the range of possible responses from participants. Above all else, your questions should never imply that there is a "right" answer. Instead, use questioning to explore participants' answers to previous questions in more detail, to focus or redirect the discussion, or to make a transition from one step in the decision-making process to the next.

Allow the Audience to Carry the Discussion   Be mindful not to exert too much control over the discussion. If the discussion is moving reasonably well, let it continue even if it is not strictly adhering to the steps outlined in the decision-making process. You can always summarize or redirect the participants if the discussion starts to ramble or stops being productive. Remember that the purpose of the case method is not to plow through the discussion to arrive at a final answer but, rather, to encourage participants to explore their own knowledge, thoughts, and values related to the issues in the case and to learn from the knowledge and perspectives of other participants. The instructor is merely a facilitator of this process, acting more as a coach than as a teacher.

Encourage Audience Members to Talk to One Another   Initially, most participants will be inclined to address their responses to the instructor. After all, most participants will have had many years of experience in educational systems where the instructor was in the position of authority. Although having participants talk with one another is not the most important outcome of the case method, it does have its purposes. In any human services field, the ability to communicate with colleagues and engage in cooperative problem solving is important. This includes both the ability to genuinely listen to other professionals and the ability to successfully communicate one's own ideas. Although it's not always easy to get audience members to communicate with one another, there are a few things you can do that might help. Ask participants to respond to one another's comments rather than allow them to present only their own ideas. This will facilitate better listening. Moving around the room may also help. Without being too obvious about it, try to position yourself off to the side of the speaker so that you are not directly in his or her line of vision, or stand directly behind other participants so that they share your line of vision with the speaker. Finally, try turning your back to the audience to write on the board or flipchart: The speaker will be compelled to find a set of eyes other than your own with which to make contact while he or she talks.

Maintain a Nonjudgmental Stance   During the discussion, be careful not to act as though you have an answer in mind and you are waiting for someone in the audience to guess what it is. This is far easier said than done. Especially at the outset of the discussion, participants will be looking for signs of your approval to judge whether they have given the "right" answer. Even the subtlest hint of disapproval on your part could cause them to shut down and back away from the discussion. For this reason, it is extremely important to pay equal respect to all participants' contributions. Look interested in what each participant has to say, ask each participant to elaborate on his ideas, then write his contributions on the board or flipchart along with the other participants' feedback. This doesn't mean that you shouldn't ever challenge the participants; but when you do, be careful not to implicitly or explicitly criticize what they have said.

Make Good Use of Boards or Flipcharts   Writing notes on a board or flipchart during a case discussion serves two major purposes. First, as stated previously, it is a way to demonstrate respect for each participant's contribution to the discussion. More important, however, it serves as a method of summarizing aspects of the discussion that you or the participants may need to refer to in a later phase of the decision-making process. For this reason, your notes should not serve just as a running account of participants' comments. Instead, as you are writing, you should be keenly aware of what information may be needed at a later time, and you should organize the participants' contributions accordingly. For example, if you open a discussion by asking for the various characters in a case story, it might prove useful to group the characters according to their affiliations (e.g., family members, informal support network, team members, professionals in other agencies). Then, when decisions need to be made about resources for implementing a plan of action, the participants can refer to this list. Another example would be to make a careful list of intervention options that are generated by the group so that these options can quickly be reviewed later in the case discussion when a choice needs to be made.

Encourage Full Participation   It is almost guaranteed that in each audience you will have at least one participant who will try to dominate the discussion and another, if not several, who will volunteer very little or nothing to the discussion. Although it is important to respect the inclinations of both, you can take some action to limit input from dominators and encourage discussion from those who are less communicative. Although a little risky, one method for handling a true dominator is to "inadvertently" stop in front of him or her as you walk around the room. With your back to the dominator for a few minutes, she is less likely to talk. You can use the resulting break in the discussion to encourage others to participate. Another strategy to limit the dominator is to recognize her contribution and then ask if there are any *other* opinions or ideas.

In some ways, less communicative participants are more of a challenge than the dominators. Making eye contact or standing in close proximity to a reluctant participant may be helpful. You can also take the risk of asking him a direct question. If you do, however, be certain that it is an easy question to answer. You might even ask the participant to think about his answer for a few minutes. Then, when you refer to the student for the answer, be absolutely certain to attend to what he says, and perhaps even make a mental note to go back to his comment at a later point in the discussion. A good rule of thumb is not to let less communicative participants sit for too long before trying to engage them. It seems that the longer they are silent, the more difficult it becomes for them to say something. Despite this "rule," don't push too hard. You never know why a particular student isn't participating, and you should respect his right to be a more passive participant. Your job is not to make reluctant participants talk. It is only to provide them with the opportunity to express their opinions and to support them if and when they do. Remember, too, that one of the reasons for encouraging full participation is to ensure that alternative perspectives are voiced and considered when students make a decision regarding the case. As long as this goal is achieved, you shouldn't worry too much about dominant or reluctant participants.

Assist Participants in Communicating   At times, a participant may have a difficult time getting her point across or may be intimidated by the strength of another participant's counterpoint. Although your role is not to protect a timid communicator or to speak for her, you should take responsibility for trying to understand what each participant is saying, and you should provide whatever assistance might be necessary to help her get her point(s) across to the rest of the group. Assistance may involve posing follow-up questions when her communications are unclear or misunderstood by others or by rewording or paraphrasing her communications. When paraphrasing, be sure to check back with the original speaker to ensure that your assumptions about what she is trying to say are correct. Remember, too, that you are trying to teach each participant to communicate for herself, so try to gradually wean her from her reliance on your assistance.

As the case discussion instructor, you may also need to teach participants to listen to one another. When students are first experiencing the case method, they may not have satisfactory listening skills. During the case discussion, they may simply wait for an opportunity to interject their opinions rather than truly attend to what the participants who have spoken before them have said. If this becomes an obvious problem, you may consider deliberately having participants respond to other students' comments rather than allowing them to say what they want. For example, if a participant starts to offer a new opinion without attending to what has just been said, you might ask, *Before you go on, what do you think about Jared's idea that . . . ?* At the very least, you will be communicating the importance of listening to others rather than just stating one's own opinion.

Stick to the Case   At some point in nearly every case discussion, participants will steer the conversation away from the case at hand. They will usually either talk about another, perhaps similar, situation that they themselves have been involved in or they will begin talking in generalities. Although some of this conversation is fine, if the discussion goes too far adrift you will want to direct the group back to the case at hand. Allow time at the close of the discussion to discuss similar situations or to make general statements or conclusions about the issues addressed in the case story.

Challenge Assumptions   Quite often, participants will make assumptions about a character or situation that are not supported by the information presented in the case story. Such assumptions are typically about the motives behind various characters' actions. If other participants do not challenge such assumptions, you may want to dispute the assumptions yourself to prevent them from being taken as facts. As always, a gentle approach is best. You may question assumptions by saying something such as, *I'm a little curious about what you just said. What makes you say _____?* *Although that might very well be true, do we really know that it is?* Because making unwarranted assumptions about the motives of others is a common mistake made by professionals in working with both families and other professionals, it is particularly important to point out these assumptions and to discuss how the assumptions might influence decisions that are made.

Listen Carefully Listening is the key to effective case method teaching, but it's not as easy as it sounds. What are participants thinking? With what issues are they struggling? Do their difficulties in application and problem solving stem from a lack of knowledge or are their roadblocks attitudinal in nature, arising from deeply held personal values and beliefs? By carefully listening to each participant, you can better understand the participant's perspective, thereby placing yourself in a better position to identify strategies that will help each person to become a more effective decision maker and service provider. Listening often involves asking questions that are designed to understand a participant's current perspective rather than questions that are intended to make the participant think in a different way. You should think of listening as an assessment technique: a method of identifying the learning needs of individual participants and your audience as a whole. You may choose to address such learning needs as they are identified or at a later, perhaps more opportune, time.

Discourage Premature Solutions Perhaps the greatest tendency of audiences is to immediately jump into offering solutions to a case. If this happens, your role is to guide the group back to earlier steps in the decision-making process. Remember, however, that you do not need to strictly adhere to the decision-making process in a step-by-step fashion. If, for example, a group is particularly eager to offer solutions, you may choose to allow this to continue for a while. At times, it may actually be a good strategy for getting the group to talk at the beginning of the case discussion. You may even want to begin writing a list of possible solutions on the board. After a few minutes, however, you should attempt to reorient the group by saying something such as, *These sound like some real possibilities for handling the situation, but let's stop here for a minute and back up a little to see what may have caused this situation to occur in the first place.* Then, you can pose a question about what has transpired so far in the case story and begin analyzing contributing factors. You may have to redirect the group more than once.

Acknowledge and Address Affect Be careful not to avoid the affective side of the discussion. For example, if a participant seems particularly adamant about offering his ideas or opinions, acknowledge this in your response to his comments by saying something such as, *You seem to feel very strongly about that. Do you know why that is?* You may have to ask follow-up questions in order to help the participant determine why he feels so strongly, as he may not know the exact source of his feelings himself. The purpose of questioning affect is not to put a participant on the "hot seat" but rather to convey a sincere interest in why he feels the way that he does and to help him figure out for himself where his emotions are coming from.

Addressing affect also includes acknowledging interpersonal conflicts if they arise during the course of the discussion. Preservice participants, in particular, may not be accustomed to handling disagreements with their peers in a public forum. They may interpret even minor differences of opinion as criticism or as personal attacks. In response, the participants may counterattack or withdraw. As the instructor, you may choose not to deal with these differences or you may provide assistance to the participants by helping them to communicate their opinions or ideas. In other instances, you may want to deal with the issue more directly by saying something such as, *You seem a little upset about what [Name] just said. Why is that?* You can then discuss the manner in which the statements were made and how they were interpreted. Deciding whether to acknowledge and address interpersonal conflicts is up to you and will be determined by your knowledge of the audience with which you are working and your purposes for using CMI.

Periodically Summarize the Discussion As is true of any conversation involving multiple people, case discussions can sometimes become rather rambling or chaotic. Participants may begin to feel as though they don't know where the discussion is headed or that it is just going around in circles. When this occurs, you should probably summarize what has been said so far and try to refocus the discussion, either back to its original path or down an entirely different avenue. Summaries provide audiences with a sense of organization, purpose, and direction for the discussion. Summaries are particularly useful in making transitions from one issue in the case to another or from one step in the decision-making process to the next.

Other Formats

For the most part, I have written the teaching notes in this instructor's manual for use in group discussions. Small-group activities, role-plays, and team simulations, however, may also be used in CMI. The format you decide on should be based on your teaching objectives. For example, if you are particularly interested in developing the participants' communication skills, the use of role play—whether pre-arranged or impromptu—may be a good choice. I have developed supplemental materials for two of the case stories in the main text ("Recipe for Rachel" and "An Uncertain Future") specifically for conducting role plays. These materials, along with recommendations for their use, can be found in this manual. I have also written case materials for conducting team simulations, though the materials are too lengthy to be included in this manual. For information on how to obtain the simulation materials, please contact me directly at the following address:

> P.J. McWilliam, Ph.D.
> Frank Porter Graham Child Development Center
> University of North Carolina
> CB#8180
> Chapel Hill, NC 27599-8180
> e-mail address: pj_mcwilliam@unc.edu

Reference

McWilliam, P.J., & Snyder, P. (1993). *Teaching through the case method.* Paper presented at the International Early Childhood Conference on Children with Special Needs, San Diego.

Leaving Wisconsin

Topics

Barriers to recommended practices, interprofessional conflicts, classroom- or center-based services, IEP, IFSP, supervision, teaming, family-centered practices, intervention planning

Synopsis

Fresh out of graduate school in Wisconsin, Liz has moved to the Deep South to start her first job as a special education teacher in a classroom for preschoolers with developmental delays. After a few weeks on the job, however, Liz has become disenchanted. Her efforts to apply recommended practices in early childhood special education by employing a family-centered approach in developing IEP goals for her students have been met with resistance from the occupational therapist and the speech-language pathologist at the school. Liz discusses her concerns with her supervisor, Helen Rohe, but Helen is only marginally supportive. Liz is left to decide for herself whether she will conform to the status quo or take action to achieve her ideals.

Major Issues

The primary issue that this story addresses is the difference that often exists between recommended practices in early intervention and what actually takes place in the "real world." Designed primarily for preservice audiences, this story reminds students that institutions may not always embrace recommended practices. Case discussion equips students with the interpersonal skills that they will need to work effectively with supervisors and team members who may not agree with their ideas. Strategies for facilitating change in program practices can also be addressed during the case discussion. Although this case was not written from the supervisor's perspective, it may be useful in teaching supervisory or managerial skills related to handling conflicts among team members or facilitating changes in program practices.

Teaching Notes

Opening questions such as, *What do you think about the situation Liz has encountered?* or, *How realistic is Liz's situation? Could it ever happen here in our state?* typically will prompt students to talk about their own experiences. Participants' stories and comments let the instructor know how knowledgeable they are about real-world practices and what their general disposition toward handling such situations might be. If nothing else, these types of questions are good for getting the discussion started.

To identify the contributing factors in this situation, the group should explore Liz's attitude and behaviors as well as the attitudes and behaviors of the other characters in the story. If time is at a premium, however, don't dwell too long on this aspect of the discussion, as you will want to dedicate a sufficient amount of class time to identifying solutions to the case. Leading questions for exploring the perspectives of characters other than Liz might include, *Why might Tanya and Allen have not cooperated fully with Liz's routines-based IEP planning? Why might Helen Rohe not have been more supportive of Liz's ideas for improving services in the preschool classroom (family-centered practices, routines-based IEPs)?* and, *Do you think Helen Rohe was being unfair to Liz?* You may need to ask additional questions to help the participants identify legitimate reasons for the characters' actions, especially if students tend to see these characters in the same negative light in which Liz sees them. Questions for identifying Liz's contributions to the situation might include the following:

- *Liz seems surprised by the reactions of the therapists and of Helen Rohe. Should she have seen this coming?*
- *Do you think that the manner in which Liz made changes was appropriate? Should she have done anything differently?*
- *Was meeting with Helen the best way for Liz to deal with her frustrations? If so, did she approach Helen in the right way?*

Sometimes revisiting the problem provides a good transition between what has happened already and what needs to be done. You can do this by saying, *At the end of the story, Liz seems to feel that the situation is rather hopeless. Is it really as bad as Liz thinks it is?* This line of questioning may be particularly important if the students have continued to view the situation solely from Liz's perspective. You may have to provide additional prompts to encourage alternative views of the situation. For example, you might say, *Is there any indication at all that Helen is even somewhat supportive of Liz's ideas?* or, *Do you think that Tanya and Allen are purposely trying to sabotage Liz's new method of developing IEPs?*

After exploring the feelings and motivations of the various characters, you will want to begin identifying solutions. You can usually initiate this discussion by posing a few simple questions, such as, *What choices does Liz have for handling the situation she's in? Should Liz just give up, turn in her resignation, and move back to Wisconsin?* or, *Should Liz give in and do things the way they have always been done at the school?* Students will typically come to the conclusion that there is hope for Liz's situation and then will begin generating possible strategies that Liz might use to accomplish her goals. At first, participants' strategies may be vague, such as suggesting that Liz should talk to Helen again or should spend more time explaining a routines-based approach to Tanya and Allen. After the group has identified several general strategies, ask them to choose an approach or a combination of approaches to use in the situation. Then try to get the group to identify more specifically what it is that they think Liz needs to do over the next few days, weeks, or months to implement the chosen strategy.

Two interesting issues that students may or may not identify on their own are 1) Liz's feelings about her assistant, Bernie, and 2) when searching for jobs, how to avoid ending up in a negative situation. Students' reactions to Bernie may vary widely, from wanting to "put her in her place" to seeing her as Liz's best source of support. If students have had strong opinions about how Helen should supervise Liz, it may be interesting to compare these views to their perspectives on how Liz should supervise Bernie. With regard to job searches, you might ask students what minimum requirements they would have for their first job after they graduate (in terms of the program's philosophy, practices, etc.). Then ask them what they could do to ensure that a job they were applying for met these requirements. You could even have students get together in small groups to develop a list of questions they might ask in an interview.

A Change of Plans

Topics

Kindergarten transitions, developmental therapies, emotional situations, low-income families, speech-language delays, clinic-based services, preschool (ages 3–5 years)

Synopsis

Elvie Bishop is going to kindergarten in 2 months. Linda Malcolm, Elvie's speech-language therapist, has worked with Elvie's mother to plan the transition to the Bishop's neighborhood elementary school in the fall. As part of the plan, Linda has scheduled an assessment for Elvie at the hospital's child development clinic. Linda knew that testing would be needed in order for Elvie to receive special education services in public school. The day after the testing has been done, Elvie's mother, Valerie Bishop, storms into the building looking for Linda Malcolm. Valerie is fuming about something she was told at the child development clinic—something about a change in Elvie's school placement in the fall.

Major Issues

The major issue that this case story addresses is kindergarten transition. This particular situation examines the responsibilities of a clinic-based therapist who is the sole service provider for a child and her family. A secondary issue that this story addresses is how a service provider should work with a family whose values and beliefs are different from those of the service provider and whose subsequent decisions don't seem to be in the best interest of the child. Finally, this story explores the issue of handling parents' emotional responses, which, in this case, are frustration and anger.

Teaching Notes

This story is particularly useful for students and professionals in the allied health fields (e.g., speech-language therapy, occupational therapy, physical therapy) or with professionals whose work involves clinic-based services; however, it also can be used with other audiences if teaching objectives include any or all of the topics described previously. You should probably include three major lines of inquiry in your discussion of this case:

1. The degree to which Linda Malcolm is doing the best she can to facilitate Elvie Bishop's transition into kindergarten
2. The manner in which the clinic staff handles Valerie's emotional behavior when she enters the center
3. What Linda Malcolm and the rest of the clinic staff should do next to defuse the situation and to facilitate Elvie's transition to kindergarten

You should consider audience composition, teaching objectives, and time constraints when determining the order in which the group should address these topics and the level of detail in which each topic should be explored. Keep in mind that audience members themselves are likely to shift the discussion from one topic to another. It's fine to let this happen; but, as the facilitator, you should carefully monitor the points that have been explored and, when necessary, gently prompt the group to return to topics that may have been shortchanged or move on to issues that have been neglected.

There are a number of ways to open the discussion of kindergarten transition and how well Linda Malcolm has followed recommended practices. For example, you might ask a broad question such as, *What do you think of Linda Malcolm as a service provider? Has she done the best job she could under the circumstances?* or, *Could anything have been done differently that might have prevented this fiasco? Was this an unavoidable situation?* Alternatively, you could immediately focus the discussion on the issue of transition by asking a more pointed question such as, *What has gone wrong in Elvie Bishop's transition to kindergarten? Could any of these problems have been avoided and, if so, how?*

A variety of issues may arise while discussing the events that led up to Valerie Bishop's outburst at the center. The audience will probably bring up many of these issues on their own; however, if there are important issues that have not been identified, you may want to prompt a discussion of them. These issues may include the following:

- *Parent participation in therapy:* Because of Valerie's interference during therapy sessions, Linda Malcolm has asked her to wait in the lounge during therapy sessions. *Was this a good idea?*
- *Parent not acting in best interest of child:* Valerie's persistent "no shows" for Elvie's therapy sessions, her choice not to enroll Elvie in preschool, and her insistence that Elvie attend kindergarten this year at the community-based school may be an indication that she is not acting in Elvie's best interests. *Should Linda have done more to persuade Valerie to attend to Elvie's needs?*
- *Role of developmental therapist in transition planning:* Linda apparently lacks pertinent information regarding community services (e.g., awareness of alternative kindergarten placements, awareness of child development clinic's waiting list for conducting child assessments). *In a case such as this one, in which a child is receiving isolated developmental therapy, to what extent is the therapist responsible for facilitating the child's transition? How much time can the therapist reasonably be expected to spend on transition issues?* Inservice audiences probably will voice concerns about billable hours, high caseloads, and the excessive responsibilities of service coordinators. If these issues are identified, you might ask participants, *Who is responsible for children such as Elvie Bishop and their families in your community, and how well does the system work?*
- *Preparing families for staff changes:* Audience members will probably identify the issue of Linda Malcolm's impending delivery. If this issue is mentioned, you might ask, *Do you think Linda's pregnancy has influenced this situation?* or, *Should Linda inform Valerie of her plans for maternity leave and give her information regarding how the birth of her baby might affect Elvie's services? If so, how much information should Linda provide to Valerie and when?*

To begin discussion about how the staff handled the mother's outburst at the center, all that probably is needed is a straightforward question: *What did you think about the responses of the various staff members to Valerie Bishop when she arrived at the center?* Alternatively, you could encourage a broader perspective on the issue by asking, *What would it be like to work with families such as the Bishops?* or, *How would you facilitate effective parent–professional partnerships with a family such as this one?* Then work toward the more specific details regarding how the various staff members could have better handled the situation with Valerie. Discussion of this topic could include interactions on the part of Linda Malcolm, the director (Ms. Anston), and the receptionist (Karen). The potential impact of interactions between nonprofessional staff and families could also be an interesting topic of discussion.

With most audiences, you should spend time discussing what should happen next in this situation. This aspect of the discussion will probably center on the topic of kindergarten placement and transition, but it may also include some discussion of how to repair and enhance the relationships between Valerie Bishop and the center staff. You can prompt discussion about the future actions of the case's characters by saying something such as, *Although we have talked a lot about what the characters in this case could or should have done differently, let's assume that the events occurred exactly as they are described in the story. What do you think should happen next?* Be sure that the discussion includes both the possibility that Linda Malcolm will be available to do something before the birth of her baby and the possibility that she won't be available.

An alternative starting point for discussing the future would be to ask, *What do you think Elvie and Valerie Bishop need now?* or, *What really would be the best placement for Elvie Bishop in the fall?* and, *Who should be responsible for determining the Bishops' needs and how these needs should be met?* Questions such as these are likely to encourage discussion of kindergarten readiness, the support needed for kindergarten success, and strategies for interagency coordination. (*Note:* You may want to assign readings on research and recommended practices related to kindergarten readiness and inclusion or be prepared to provide this information to the audience during the discussion.)

Money Matters

Topics

Community resources, family-centered practices, intervention planning, multiple and severe disabilities, interagency coordination, family support services, home-based services, assistive technology, preschool (ages 3–5 years), middle- to upper-income families, siblings

Synopsis

Blair Seagroves is 4 years old. Despite her severe cerebral palsy and the fact that she does not speak, it is becoming increasingly obvious that she is a bright little girl. Much of Blair's progress can be attributed to the dedicated effort of her mother, Judy Seagroves. Anne-Marie has been working with the family since they moved from Minnesota to Forest Hills. Over the past few months, Anne-Marie and Judy have been working together to develop an augmentative communication system for Blair. This case story describes Anne-Marie's most recent visit to the Seagroves's home. During this visit, Judy informs Anne-Marie that family finances may no longer allow her to be a stay-at-home mom. Judy also raises concerns about her 6-year-old son Nick's problems in first grade. These new concerns force Anne-Marie to revise her strategies for working with the Seagroves family and challenge her knowledge of the resources that are available in the Forest Hills community.

Major Issues

This case story was designed primarily for teaching audiences about the availability and use of community resources for young children with special needs and their families. Through engaging in the case discussion and completing the associated teaching activity, participants should develop skills in identifying family priorities and in planning strategies to accomplish these priorities. In this situation, family priorities include obtaining necessary services for a preschooler with multiple and severe disabilities (e.g., assistive technology, adaptive equipment, child care, transportation), family financial assistance, and help with identifying and addressing the learning and behavior problems of an undiagnosed school-age sibling.

Teaching Notes

I originally designed this story for use in preservice training, its purpose being to make students aware of the need for *all* early intervention professionals to know about the resources and services that may or may not be available to meet a variety of child and family needs. This case and its accompanying teaching activity are particularly well-suited for use with interdisciplinary audiences. Use of this case in inservice training activities, however, may also be beneficial in increasing awareness of community resources, particularly when the audience includes representatives from various agencies within the same community.

For less-experienced audiences (e.g., preservice), you will probably want to conduct this activity in two sessions, separated by enough time to allow the participants to complete the group assignment "Money Matters" (pp. 70–73). During the first session, you should conduct a preliminary discussion of the case story and assign students to groups. The case discussion should follow the questions provided at the end of the case story, with the primary objectives of the discussion being to generate a list of possible family concerns, resources, and priorities and to provide participants with some leads for beginning their investigation of community resources. (*Note:* You may ask participants to complete some or all of the discussion questions prior to the first session.) If necessary, provide groups with class time to plan their assignment (e.g., deciding on individual responsibilities). During the next class session, discussion of the case story should be resumed, using the information that the various groups gathered while completing the assignment. For experienced interagency audiences, there will probably not be a need for two sessions. Such audiences should already know a great deal of information about community resources and therefore should not need time to gather such information.

For preservice audiences, the primary purpose of the second session is for groups and individuals to share the information that they have obtained and to recount the experiences they had while acquiring the information. This may be done by having each group take a turn at reporting their various findings or by using the previously generated list of family concerns to guide the discussion, with each group reporting on the resources they investigated that were related to the various family concerns as they are discussed. Even participants with considerable experience in early intervention often report being astonished by the lack of resources available in the community. Resources or services that experienced participants had taken for granted as being available and useful to children and families often are found to be unavailable, are in short supply, are extremely expensive, or don't provide the type of assistance that participants originally thought they provided. Equally as often, participants will report their surprise at the difficulty that they encountered while trying to obtain the information they needed, offering tales about unanswered telephone calls, agencies failing to return their calls, long hours spent in the ethereal pathways of "hold," or getting the "regal runaround" from person to person or agency to agency. Other surprises that participants may report include application forms that are nearly impossible to complete but that must be filled out before the client can be told about eligibility requirements, getting varying information from different people within the same agency, and encountering people on the telephone who are curt or outright rude. In a past discussion of this case, after telling about his experiences, one student exclaimed, "I don't know how parents can be expected to get *any* services. After a while, I just felt like throwing in the towel. No wonder parents are acting so angry by the time they get to us!"

A final topic of discussion could be how the information regarding community resources might be used in working with the Seagroves family. This can be done during the preliminary discussion of the case story or after the discussion of community resources. This aspect of the discussion could include

- How to identify what Judy Seagroves's highest priorities really are: *What is she most concerned about? What would be most helpful to her?*
- How to determine what information Judy Seagroves wants and how much information should be provided to her at one time: *Where should the service provider begin?*

- How much help should the service provider offer Judy Seagroves in finding out more about community resources or in gaining access to these resources for Judy?

If your teaching objectives also include instruction in family-centered intervention planning and/or communication skills in working with families, you might consider conducting a follow-up activity in which participants role-play a conversation. The purpose of the role play would be to practice effective ways to focus family priorities and, when appropriate, to share with "Judy" information about community resources. Such a role play could be done either with pairs of students (playing the roles of Judy and Anne-Marie) or through a team simulation in which one member of each group (use the groups that were identified for investigating community resources) assumes the role of Judy Seagroves and the other members of the group act as an early intervention team responding to Judy's concerns and priorities.

Mother of Two

Topics

Teenage parenting, individualized family service plan (IFSP), family support services, sexual abuse, confidentiality, low-income families, service coordination, home-based services, infancy (from birth to age 3 years), urban environments, personal safety

Synopsis

Harrison Street, where 19-year-old Crystal Matthews lives with her two small children, is renowned for its violence, drugs, and gangs. Rhonda Spelling has developed a trusting relationship with this young mother and wants to do whatever she can to help Crystal succeed. Rhonda has been visiting Crystal because Crystal's infant son, Corey, is at risk for developmental delays; but Rhonda is also concerned about Crystal's daughter who will be entering kindergarten in the fall and doesn't seem to be ready. Rhonda's overriding concern, however, is the safety of this family, so she has initiated the process of helping Crystal obtain better housing. In doing so, Rhonda has made a promise to Crystal—a promise not to tell who the father of Crystal's children is. Rhonda is shocked when she discovers that Crystal is a victim of incest.

Major Issues

The issue of incest in this story and the young mother's desire to keep it a secret is dramatic, but the central issue is really that of teenage mothers living in poverty. As such, this is an excellent case story for

- Exploring family strengths and needs
- Exploring and securing community resources to meet multiple family needs
- Discussing issues related to service coordination
- Identifying strategies for developing effective partnerships with young and inexperienced mothers

Teaching Notes

Several other stories in this collection also address the issue of teenage motherhood ("Passing Time," "Daria's Silence," and "The Need to Know"). Depending on your teaching objectives, you may want to review these stories and use them instead of or in addition to "Mother of Two." For example, although the young mothers in "Daria's Silence" and "Passing Time" also live in poverty, Daria's anger and Arora's distancing contrast sharply with the openness that Crystal Matthews displays in her relationship with the home-based service provider in "Mother of Two." Legal and ethical issues also arise in these other stories that are similar in some ways to the issues in "Mother of Two," yet different in other ways. Again, comparing the three stories may provoke an interesting discussion and at the same time aid in accomplishing certain teaching objectives.

The issues in "Mother of Two" can be classified into three broad categories:

1. Parent–professional relationships and communication
2. Family support and service coordination
3. The issue of incest and Crystal's desire to keep it confidential

As usual, there will be considerable overlap among these issues in the discussion; however, you may want to keep these categories in mind to ensure that the issues that are most relevant to your teaching objectives are covered satisfactorily. Consequently, your teaching objectives may influence the order in which you discuss these issues and the amount of time that you choose to devote to each topic.

To begin the discussion of parent–professional relationships and communication skills, you might ask a broad, open-ended question such as, *What do you think about the way that the home visitor, Rhonda Spelling, interacts with Crystal in this story?* Or you could take a more academic approach by asking, *Does Rhonda Spelling employ a family-centered approach in her interactions with this teenage mother? Can you identify specific examples of how Rhonda Spelling implemented principles of a family-centered approach while working with Crystal?* You might choose to discuss the way that Rhonda interacts with Crystal (e.g., what she says to her) and Rhonda's overall style of conducting home visits (e.g., folding clothes with Crystal). The discussion might also address the appropriateness of Rhonda's other actions (e.g., *Should Rhonda have brought up the issue of finding safer housing to Crystal? Is Rhonda encouraging Crystal's dependence by making all of the telephone calls and appointments for Crystal?*).

If you are interested in including the IFSP process as part of the discussion, you might then ask, *What do you think Crystal Matthews's concerns and priorities are?* and, *What additional concerns would you have about this family if you were the home visitor? . . . How would you discuss these concerns with Crystal?* List all of the participants' suggestions on the board as they are identified so that participants can refer to them later.

In reading this case, the participants will actually learn very little about the needs of the story's target child, Corey, aside from the fact that he appears to have some feeding difficulties. Instead the story focuses on the multiple needs of the family, thus raising questions about the availability of community resources and the need for service coordination across agencies. An interesting topic of discussion for this case is who should be responsible for securing and coordinating resources for this family? *Should Rhonda assume responsibility for helping Crystal find better housing? . . . for Pepper's transition into kindergarten? . . . for the welfare of Crystal's sister, Neecy? . . . for addressing Crystal's past sexual abuse?* Underlying all of these questions are two larger questions: *Who, ideally, should be the service coordinator for Crystal and her family? Rhonda? Celine Garner? An independent agency?* and, *How would Rhonda's role and responsibility for handling these issues be different if she was or was not the identified service coordinator for the Matthews family?* Especially with inservice audiences, you might choose to extend this conversation to include a discussion of how the participants' own service systems operate in terms of responsibility for service coordination.

You may want to extend the discussion of the Matthews's much-needed family support, multiple agency involvement, and service coordination into identifying the specific types of agencies that might provide services to the Matthews family. One way to begin this discussion is to return to the list of family priorities and professional concerns that the group identified earlier in the discussion, and ask the group to identify the type(s) of community agency(s) that might be able to address each concern. Another strategy is to conduct the group activity developed for "Money Matters" (pp. 70–73). The characteristics of your audience and your teaching objectives will determine whether it would be worthwhile to take the time that is needed to complete this group activity.

At some point in the discussion, you will probably want to discuss the issue of incest. You can begin this discussion by asking the group about the legal and ethical issues surrounding Crystal's request to keep her sexual abuse a secret. Questions for prompting this aspect of the discussion might include the following:

- *Is Rhonda breaking any laws by keeping Crystal's secret? If so, should Rhonda keep her promise anyway?*
- *Even if Rhonda isn't legally required to report the incest, should she tell someone about it? If so, who should she tell and why?*
- *If Rhonda breaks her promise by telling someone about the incest, should she tell Crystal what she has done? If so, what should she say? How might this affect Rhonda and Crystal's relationship?*
- *If Rhonda decides not to tell anyone about the incest, should she try to convince Crystal to tell someone? If so, who should Crystal tell?*
- *Can Rhonda presume that Crystal's younger sister, Neecy, is safe from being sexually abused by their father? If not, is Rhonda under any legal or ethical obligation to ensure Neecy's protection?*

A second, related area of questioning that you might want to initiate is what, if anything, Rhonda should do about her knowledge of the incest, regardless of whether she tells anyone else about it. Specific questions for facilitating this aspect of the discussion might include, *Should Rhonda have any further discussions with Crystal regarding Crystal's sexual abuse? If so, what should Rhonda say to Crystal? How comfortable would you feel about talking to Crystal regarding this issue?*

Finally, at some point during the case discussion, you may want to address the issue of personal safety that is brought up in this case story. You might ask, *How would you feel about making home visits in an area like Harrison Street? How can we protect ourselves from harm and still provide quality services to families like the Matthews family?*

Absent Mother

Topics

Substance abuse, child abuse and neglect, low-income families, infancy (from birth to age 3 years), home-based services, extended families, personal safety, prenatal drug exposure

Synopsis

Chauncey, who is now 6 months old, was exposed prenatally to illegal drugs. Immediately following Chauncey's birth, his mother, Angela, sought treatment for her addiction and succeeded in becoming drug-free. Lynne, an early interventionist, has been providing home-based services to the family for several months. Visits with Angela and Chauncey have gone quite well until recently. Over the past few weeks, Angela has not been home for Lynne's scheduled visits. On the day that this story takes place, Lynne arrives to find Chauncey and his two sisters at their great-grandmother's apartment, a few blocks down the street from Angela's. Chauncey's great-grandmother Frances tells Lynne that Angela is using drugs again. She shares her concerns about Angela's addiction and its effect on her ability to be a competent parent. Frances also talks to Lynne about actions she can take to get her granddaughter off drugs once and for all.

Major Issues

The major issues in this case story center around Angela's drug abuse. First and foremost, the safety and well-being of Angela's three young children is brought into question. Second, Lynne must decide how to approach the mother about her obvious relapse into drug use. Legal issues related to suspected child neglect, as well as the potential impact of Lynne's decisions on her relationship with Angela, must be considered. This story also touches on issues related to roles and relationships with extended family members, the multiple impacts of poverty, and the personal safety of service providers.

Teaching Notes

Although the decisions that the interventionist in this case story faces are difficult and the ramifications of the decisions potentially great, the story itself is not very complicated. Some background information about the family as well as a brief history of service provision have been included, but few other details have been provided. As a result, the reader knows very little about the multiplicity of factors that may be contributing to this situation.

The relatively uncomplicated nature of this story makes it suitable for a fairly straightforward discussion of the story's central issues: drug abuse and child neglect. Consequently, you might choose to take a more focused approach in opening up the discussion than you might typically take. Opening comments and questions can be used to immediately orient the group to the issue of child neglect. For example, you might begin by saying, *At the end of the story, Lynne seems concerned about the safety of Angela's three children. Even so, she appears to have decided not to take any further action until the next day. If you had been the home visitor in this situation, would you have done the same thing?* Participants are likely to provide a variety of responses, ranging from complete agreement with Lynne's decision to saying that they would have immediately called law enforcement or child protective services. If you don't get a variety of responses, you might encourage further discussion and alternative opinions by asking follow-up questions such as, *Just how safe are these three young children? Who would be responsible if anything happened to the children overnight?* or, *If you reported Angela to protective services, what would protective services be likely to do? Would reporting Angela have any impact on Lynne's ability to provide effective services to this family?*

Legal issues related to reporting suspected child neglect are bound to be raised by the participants as the discussion proceeds. If not, you should probably introduce these issues through questioning. The more experienced the audience, the greater the chance there is that they will know what the law says and how it is usually interpreted. Experienced audiences are also likely to know how the protective services system in their state or community typically operates; however, you will probably need to provide this information to less-experienced audiences by assigning readings prior to the case discussion or by conducting a mini-lecture when the issue arises during the course of the discussion. For example, if it becomes apparent that audience members don't know what the laws are regarding reporting suspected neglect, you can show a prepared flipchart that outlines the legal requirements in your state. The group can then debate whether Lynne would really be required by law to report the incident described in the story. Discussion of Lynne's legal obligation to report the incident may raise yet another issue: *How might Lynne, if she reports Angela, affect Angela's relationship with her grandmother?* This question may arise because Frances told Lynne that the children were left alone in Angela's apartment; Lynne did not actually witness this situation herself.

Before deciding what Lynne should do next, you may want to back up and discuss earlier events in the story. In the case story, Lynne had noticed changes in Angela's behavior over a period of at least several weeks before the critical incident took place. To begin discussion of this aspect of the story, you might ask, *Should Lynne have seen this situation coming? Was there anything that Lynne could have done differently that might have kept the situation from happening?* These questions are likely to generate discussion about the signs, symptoms, and treatment of drug addiction; therefore, you may want to gather some information about these topics to share with the group during the discussion or hand out a list of references that the students can consult to learn more about drug addiction. (*Note:* Readings on prenatal drug exposure should also be included in the list of references.) Issues concerning family support, interagency coordination, and confidentiality are also likely to arise during this part of the discussion. Depending on the available time and your teaching objectives, you might also consider broaching the issues surrounding Lynne's discussion of Angela's problems with Frances (e.g. confidentiality, Lynne's role and involvement with extended family members). This issue, however, may also be introduced while exploring potential solutions.

To begin the process of identifying solutions, you might pose a question such as, *Regardless of what Lynne should or shouldn't have done in the past, the most important question is what should she do next?* As always, try to obtain at least several possible alternatives from the audience before allowing participants to decide on a definite course of action for Lynne. Have the group discuss the pros and cons of each alternative in terms of the possible effects the alternative would have on Lynne's relationship with Angela and the solution's possible short- and long-term effects on Chauncey and Angela's other two children.

As the group begins to zero in on a solution(s), prompt them to be specific about what Lynne's course of action should be and to consider strongly the possible consequences of each proposed action. For example, if the group leans toward reporting Angela to child protective services or warning her that this could happen, you might ask, *If Lynne reports Angela to the authorities, should she tell Angela about it? And, if so, what exactly should she say to Angela?* or, *If Lynne decides to warn or threaten Angela that she could be reported for child neglect, how should Lynne state this warning to Angela?* If the group decides that Lynne needs to address the issue of drug use with Angela, you might ask, *How could Lynne initiate such a conversation with Angela?* and, *What exactly should Lynne say?* You should also have participants consider how Angela might respond to their proposed strategy. For example, you might ask, *I can understand why you think that Lynne needs to discuss this issue with Angela, but I can't help but wonder how a presumably young, single, African American mother of three children who is living in a relatively impoverished—and perhaps unsafe—urban neighborhood and is involved in illegal drug use is going to respond to such a conversation?* (*Note:* If your teaching objectives include issues related to cultural diversity, at some point you might ask whether the race or ethnicity of the home visitor in this situation is likely to make a difference.)

Further discussion of Angela's situation may provide the group with an opportunity to address this family's need for resources and services beyond those related to Chauncey's special needs and Angela's drug problem (e.g., financial needs, child care and enrichment for all three children, medical and dental care, employment). Issues of interagency coordination and collaboration might also emerge. If appropriate, you could also introduce the issue of working in neighborhoods such as the one where Angela lives (i.e., personal safety).

Finally, you may want to initiate a discussion about Lynne's role with Frances if this issue has not been addressed already. You might ask, *Should Lynne discuss Angela and her children with Frances? Should Lynne answer Frances's questions about what she can or should do to help Angela? Should Lynne keep Frances informed about the decisions she makes regarding Angela? What should Lynne's role with Frances be in the future, and how should Lynne determine this?*

In extended training activities, you may want to use the case story "Passing Time" in conjunction with "Absent Mother" to initiate a discussion of the different circumstances surrounding suspected child neglect cases and how these differences might influence decision-making in reporting and handling such situations. "Passing Time" is a story about a teenage mother and, unlike "Absent Mother," does not include the issue of drug addiction.

c h a p t e r   6

Passing Time

Topics

Child abuse and neglect, teenage parenting, extended families, infancy (from birth to age 3 years), home-based services, premature birth, growth delay

Synopsis

Arora Steele is only 17 years old and is already a mother. Her son, Jamille, was born 2 months prematurely. Although his health has improved, Jamille is still small, and there are concerns about his overall developmental progress. Arora lives with her mother, Mavis Steele, and her 6-year-old sister, Tonya. Without Mavis's help, it is doubtful that Jamille would be progressing as quickly as he has been. Rachel Thomas, the home visitor, is concerned that Arora's interest in her son has declined over the past few weeks. Rachel is truly alarmed, however, when she arrives for a visit and finds that Arora isn't home and has left Tonya in charge of 7-month-old Jamille.

Major Issues

The most pressing problem in this case story is the fact that the young mother, Arora, has left her infant son alone in the care of a 6-year-old child. Rachel Thomas, the home visitor, who has encountered this situation, must decide whether the situation constitutes child neglect and, if it does, what she should do about it. This problem, however, may be related to a more central issue in the story—working with teenage mothers. The home visitor in this story is faced with numerous challenges, including how to foster parent–child attachment, how to teach basic child care skills, how to develop effective parent–professional relationships, and how to work with both the teen mother and the grandmother when both are involved in the care of the child.

Teaching Notes

This story is similar to "Absent Mother" in that both cases confront the issues of child neglect and of children being left in the care of other children. In this story, however, the circumstances surrounding the suspected neglect don't appear to be quite as dire. Whereas the neglect of the children in "Absent Mother" is related to the mother's drug abuse, the reason for the neglect in this story seems to be more a matter of teenage irresponsibility or incompetence. Nevertheless, in this case, the professional is actually a witness to the fact that a child has been left in the home without a responsible adult. These differences should be taken into consideration when choosing between the two case stories. It may, however, be educational to discuss both of the stories with the same audience in order to compare the participants' reactions to each story and their subsequent decisions regarding the actions that they think the characters in each story should take.

There are three main issues that should be covered in the discussion of this case story:

1. How Rachel has worked with the family in the past
2. How Rachel should handle the current situation
3. What strategies Rachel might employ in her future work with this family

The first two issues may be discussed in reverse order if that better suits your teaching objectives.

The purpose of discussing Rachel's prior work with the family is to identify some of the factors that may have contributed to the current situation. You could begin the discussion by asking broad questions such as, *What do you think of the way in which Rachel has worked with this family in the past?* and, *Was there anything that you would have done differently if you had been the service provider?* Another way to pinpoint any contributing factors would be to say, *Near the end of the story, Rachel seems to feel that she may be partly to blame for Arora's absence. What was it that she thought she might have done wrong? Do you agree?* Questions such as these should uncover a variety of issues, including Mavis's persistent criticism of Arora; Rachel's "overreliance" on Mavis; Rachel's willingness to let Arora leave the house during home visits; and, perhaps, Rachel's avoidance of confronting Arora when she first noticed Arora's waning interest in Jamille. If some of these issues are not broached by participants, you might introduce them yourself by saying, *Didn't Rachel also question whether she and Mavis had perhaps made Arora feel incompetent in caring for her own son? What made her think that this might be true? Do you agree?* To direct the discussion to the topic of neglect, you might ask, *Regardless of what Rachel should or should not have done in the past, the fact remains that Arora has left Jamille at home with Tonya. Rachel has to make some decisions about how to handle this situation. What are Rachel's choices? What do you think she should do?* As the discussion ensues, ask the group to consider the possibility that Arora is in the arriving elevator and the possibility that she is not.

The legal requirements for reporting suspected neglect are bound to arise during the discussion. If not, broach the topic yourself. Even experienced professionals may not know what the law actually states, how reporting should be handled, and what the consequences of being reported actually are. Know the answers to these questions yourself, and be prepared to provide this information to the group (e.g., flipchart, mini-lecture, handout). Another possibility would be to have some or all members of the group research these issues prior to the discussion. It might also be interesting to have a student or a group of students research the law and then interview professionals in child protective services agencies to discover the methods and ramifications of child neglect reporting. This could be done prior to or following the case discussion.

Discussion of whether Rachel should report Arora's neglect of the children should include consideration of the potential impact it could have on both Arora and Mavis. Participants should also take into consideration the effects that reporting Arora would have on Mavis's and Arora's relationships with Rachel. Depending on your audience and the direction of the discussion, you might also ask, *Even if Rachel thinks that she should, by law, report Arora, should she consider not doing it if she believes that the situation will not be repeated and that reporting Arora would do more harm than good?* Regardless of how the group decides Rachel should handle the current situation, you should press them further into identifying how they would actually implement their decision. If they decide Rachel should report Arora, should she tell Arora? And, if so, what would she say? Should Rachel tell Mavis that she reported Arora? If the group decides not to report Arora, however, should Rachel confront Arora about the issue? If so, how?

If time permits and it is important to your teaching objectives, the next step in the discussion might be to determine how Rachel should work with this family in the future. For example, you might ask, *When this whole incident is over, what changes, if any, should Rachel make in how she works with this family?* Another way to introduce this topic would be to ask, *What do you think it's like being Arora? What do you think she might want or need, and how could you determine this?* Any or all of these questions are designed to make the participants consider other resources and services that might be useful to the family and to identify strategies for working effectively with teenage mothers. If the issue of working with teenage mothers is a high priority in your teaching objectives, you could provide research information, program descriptions, and evaluation data about this topic via assigned readings or a mini-lecture.

Proceed with Caution

Topics

Inclusion, consultation, cultural diversity, child care quality, integrated therapies, preschool (ages 3–5 years), classroom- or center-based services, friendships

Synopsis

Three-year-old Nathan Hammond is a new referral to the Preschool Inclusion Program (PIP), and Carrie Richards has been assigned to his case. Early in the morning, Carrie arrives at Smiling Faces Day Care, where Nathan is enrolled. Carrie has never been to this preschool before and is in for a cultural awakening. Although the director, Violet Webster, is friendly to Carrie, the other caregivers at Smiling Faces Day Care are less than welcoming. Carrie is also unprepared for the rigid structure of the program and the strictness of the caregivers. Above all, Carrie is concerned that the staff and other children are not including Nathan as they should be, and Carrie questions whether staff members are amenable to making changes.

Major Issues

This story addresses two major issues regarding the inclusion of a child with special needs in a regular child care environment. First, the quality of the child care environment itself is questionable and, therefore, so is its appropriateness as a placement for Nathan. The types of activities that take place in the child care center and the manner in which the staff interact with the children are not in line with recommended practices. The second major issue is the role of Carrie Richards, the consultant, in this environment. In the story, the reactions of the child care staff to Carrie's presence and the behaviors and feelings of Carrie, herself, provide fertile ground for discussing effective consultation strategies.

Teaching Notes

This case story provides a detailed description of the child–staff interactions and the daily routines that take place within a regular child care environment. The case also provides a detailed description of the caregivers' reactions to a consultant who comes to the center to work with a child with special needs. Such detail allows the discussion to go beyond decisions exclusively about placement to include decisions about specific intervention strategies (e.g., functional skills, integrated therapy, social inclusion) and strategies for providing effective consultation.

The list of discussion questions found at the end of the story provides one line of inquiry for facilitating the discussion. You may, of course, decide to focus more on some questions than on others, depending on your audience and your teaching objectives. The guidelines that follow are, in large part, based on this original list of questions.

You may want to begin the discussion by assessing where your audience stands with regard to the quality of care provided at Smiling Faces Day Care. Reactions to the quality of care can be diverse: Experienced audiences will perhaps be more positive about what goes on at Violet's place than less experienced, more idealistic, audiences. To assess their reactions, you can begin with a simple question such as, *So, how would you like to have Carrie Richards's job of working with Nathan at Violet's child care center?* or, *What did you think about what goes on behind the door of Smiling Faces Day Care?* If participants give only general answers, such as, *It's not a very good environment for any child,* or, *It's not so bad. . . . I've seen a lot worse,* be sure to prompt them for more specific reasons for their answers. Also be sure to encourage alternative viewpoints. For example, if the initial responses are extremely negative, you might ask, *Is it really all that bad? Are there any redeeming qualities about this center?* As the discussion proceeds, you may want to make two lists on the board or flipchart—a list of concerns and a list of strengths—related to the quality of care at the center. Another way to generate this list would be to begin the discussion by asking, *What are Carrie's concerns about the overall quality of care provided at Smiling Faces Day Care? Do you share these concerns?* and, *What additional concerns do you have?* (Note: The discussion of quality should include the physical environment, the staff's interactions with the children, and the routines or child activities.)

If you are interested in exploring the influence of cultural values and beliefs in this situation, this may be a good point to do so. For example you could ask, *Why do you think Violet has chosen to operate her child care center in the manner that she has—teaching children their letters, numbers, and colors . . . the staff's methods of discipline . . . the types of relationships she has with the children's families?* You might also ask, *Do you think there are any parents who would actually choose to send their child to Violet's if they could afford other child care? Why?*

If you haven't already discussed Carrie's concerns about Nathan's treatment at the center, your next step could be to have participants generate a list of potential concerns. The most obvious of Carrie's concerns is the use of various restraint methods by the center's caregivers to "protect" Nathan (e.g., the highchair, the swing, keeping Nathan inside with Leanne during outdoor time). Again, you should ask participants if they share Carrie's concerns and if they have any additional concerns about the way that the caregivers at the center handle Nathan. You might also ask, *Why do you think the staff has taken the approach they have in dealing with Nathan? Do their reasons justify their actions?* and, *What alternatives do they have available to them?* Finally, depending on the degree of negativity expressed in the group's responses, you might ask if there is *anything* that the participants like about the manner in which the staff interact with or otherwise handle Nathan.

At this point, you could continue the discussion about Nathan by asking, *Is this placement a complete failure for Nathan, or is there some chance that the placement can be salvaged? In other words, should Carrie give up on Smiling Faces Day Care altogether and concentrate her efforts on finding an alternative placement for Nathan?* Keep in mind that by asking these questions you will be moving the group toward the identification of solutions. If consultation strategies are included in your teaching objectives, you may want to limit this aspect of the discussion, or postpone it entirely, until after discussing Carrie's contributions to the situation.

To begin the discussion about consultation, you might say, *Leanne and Diana certainly didn't extend a warm welcome to Carrie. Why do you think they acted so unfriendly?* Or you could ask, *What did you think about the way in which Carrie conducted herself on her first visit to Violet's child care center?* During this phase of the discussion, you should try to accomplish two things, both related to the role of the consultant. First, you should ask the group to explore the staff's reaction to Carrie's visit. *To what extent did the staff understand why Carrie was there?* This discussion point should include Leanne's and Diana's degree of understanding as well as Violet's. For example, when Carrie first arrives at the center, Violet asks, "Did you want to take [Nathan] off by himself?" and as Carrie is leaving she says, "We'll do whatever we can to help you out." Second, you might want to have the group explore how Carrie might have contributed to the staff's reactions and what she could have done differently to establish her role as a consultant. The group may also identify additional contributing factors, such as the possibility that Leanne and Diana feel that their skills in working with Nathan and the other children are being scrutinized or criticized, or the possibility that Carrie is just experiencing the awkwardness that is inherent in any new relationship.

The next step is to have participants identify potential solutions to the situation. This can be accomplished by saying, *At the conclusion of her visit to Violet's place, Carrie has a number of thoughts about what she should do next. Some of her ideas include speaking to Nathan's parent(s), talking to her supervisor, Gloria, or finding another child care placement for Nathan. Are any of these thoughts good ideas? What other options does Carrie have?* As always, ensure that a sufficient number of options and viewpoints have been expressed and that the pros and cons of each option have been discussed before allowing the group to settle on one solution. If the group leans toward finding an alternative placement for Nathan, you might want to push the group a bit by asking, *What should Carrie do if finding another placement for Nathan is not an option—if Nathan has to stay at Violet's for at least the time being?*

In some situations, you may want to end the discussion at this point. If, however, your teaching objectives include the development of more specific intervention-planning skills (e.g., embedding interventions into daily routines, integrated therapy), you may want to supplement the story with a mock assessment report(s) on Nathan or a mock IEP. The group could then be asked to discuss how Carrie could implement interventions and accomplish Nathan's developmental goals within the context of Smiling Faces Day Care. (*Note:* See also "Beyond Duty," a sequel to this story, in which additional consultation issues are addressed.)

chapter 8

Beyond Duty

Topics

Consultation, professional boundaries, confidentiality, kindergarten transitions, preschool (ages 3–5 years), classroom- or center-based services

Synopsis

Carrie Richards has been working with Nathan Hammond as part of the Preschool Inclusion Program at Smiling Faces Day Care, and she has scheduled an appointment to discuss Nathan's upcoming needs with the director, Violet Webster. As Carrie arrives for the meeting, Violet is handling an emergency. One of Violet's former preschoolers has been suspended from kindergarten for behavior problems, and his grandmother is looking for a place to take him while she is at work. Although Carrie has never provided services for this child, she is drawn into the situation. This case story may be used as a sequel to "Proceed with Caution," or it may stand alone.

Major Issues

This case story addresses the ethical issues of professional boundaries and confidentiality in providing consultation services within center-based programs. The primary issue raised in this story is the extent to which consultants working with specific children in a center-based program should involve themselves with staff members' concerns about other children or families in the same program. Staff concerns in this story are related to a child's transition into kindergarten.

Teaching Notes

This is not a particularly complex situation; therefore, little time needs to be devoted to analyzing the factors that contributed to the situation. Instead, this story lends itself to a more theoretical discussion of the ethical issues one might encounter while providing consultation services. You might begin the discussion with the most obvious question: *Should Carrie become involved in the situation concerning Davin and, if so, to what degree?* Encourage alternative perspectives and have participants provide justification for their opinions.

Following adequate discussion of this case's particular situation, you might want to pose several other hypothetical situations in which a consultant is told information about a child or a family and asked for his or her opinion or assistance. For example, you might ask, *Suppose Violet asks Carrie what she should do about a 2-year-old in the center who is biting other children. Should Carrie provide any assistance?* Use examples that could easily be handled by the professional discipline(s) represented in your audience as well as examples that would not be within the participants' areas of expertise. By asking participants to consider a variety of situations, they will be challenged to define ethical standards by which they can judge their own professional conduct related to consultation boundaries. Perhaps more important, participants will come to the realization that these boundaries are not black and white.

Two important issues are likely to emerge during the discussion of this case: First, in order to provide effective consultation in child care centers, professionals must develop good working relationships with the child care staff. Furthermore, the more extensive and frequent the consultation, the more immersed in the child care the professional is likely to become. In setting professional boundaries, a consultant must take care not to sacrifice the relationship that he or she has worked so hard to establish. Second, with regard to the establishment of relationships, the question arises, *Who* is the recipient of the consultation services: the child or the child care staff? In this particular situation, is Carrie there to assist Nathan Hammond or to assist the staff at Smiling Faces Day Care Center so that they may, in turn, help Nathan? The distinction is usually blurred.

An interesting assignment to follow-up discussions of "Proceed with Caution" and "Beyond Duty" would be to have individuals or small groups write a short paper (one or two pages) entitled, "A Code of Conduct for Professionals Providing Consultation in Child Care Centers."

The Need to Know

Topics

Human immunodeficiency virus (HIV) and acquired immunodeficiency syndrome (AIDS), confidentiality, personal safety, teenage parenting, infancy (from birth to age 3 years), middle- to upper-income families, home-based services, classroom- or center-based services, emotional situations

Synopsis

Paula Goldman is a young, single mother who lives at home with her parents. Her son Jeffrey was born prematurely and has hemiplegia due to complications he experienced during his stay in the neonatal intensive care unit. Sherra Nowell-Hill has been providing home-based services to the Goldmans since shortly after Jeffrey's homecoming. Jeffrey is now 17 months old, and Paula is interested in finding a child care center for him to attend. Sherra meets with Paula to discuss child care options but is unprepared for the news that Paula delivers—both she and Jeffrey are HIV-positive. Furthermore, Paula wants their conditions to remain a secret.

Major Issues

The major issues that this case story addresses center on Paula's desire to keep secret the fact that she and Jeffrey are HIV-positive. Legal and ethical issues regarding confidentiality also arise, as do issues of personal safety for service providers.

Teaching Notes

Paula and Jeffrey belie the stereotypes associated with HIV and AIDS. Paula comes from a well-educated, middle-class family that is extremely supportive of Paula and her son Jeffrey. This case provides a good opportunity to remind trainees that anyone can contract HIV, and service providers may not always know when they have had contact with someone who has the virus. In other words, this is a good case for discussing the myths and realities of HIV and for reinforcing the need for all service providers to adhere to universal safety precautions.

Although this story focuses on the issues of confidentiality and safety, it also deals with relationships between families and service providers. If your teaching objectives include communication skills and strategies for developing effective partnerships with parents, it might be a good idea to begin the case discussion by addressing these issues before opening up the discussion to the more obvious topics. For example, you might begin with questions such as the following:

- *What do you think about the way Sherra handled the situation with Paula Goldman at the hotel restaurant?*
- *What specifically did Sherra say or do that you thought was effective?*
- *Did Sherra apply any principles of family-centered service provision in her interactions with Paula? If so, what were they?*
- *Is there anything that you would have done or said differently in this situation?*

At this point in the discussion, you could also consider introducing the general topic of how to handle emotionally charged situations with families effectively. This topic may be particularly important for preservice audiences and for relatively new service providers participating in in-service training.

Before delving too deeply into discussions of confidentiality and decisions about what Sherra should do next, it might be a valuable exercise to encourage the group to explore what the potential risks actually are in this situation. Several questions that the instructor might ask include the following:

- *If Jeffrey does attend the child care center, what will be the actual risks to the care providers and the other children in his classroom?*
- *Toward the end of the story, Sherra asks herself whether she has put herself and her unborn child at risk. To what degree could this be true?*
- *What might be the potential risks to Paula's parents and anyone else who plays a role in Jeffrey's life?*
- *What are the risks to Jeffrey if he is enrolled in a child care center?*

This last question is especially thought-provoking because the health risks to Jeffrey himself may, in fact, be significantly greater than the health risks to the caregivers and to the other children. Questions such as these ensure that trainees have accurate knowledge about HIV and AIDS. A mini-lecture outlining the facts about HIV and AIDS may be necessary if it becomes obvious that the group is ill-informed.

The following questions could be included in discussion regarding how to handle Paula's expressed desire to keep secret the fact that she and Jeffrey are HIV positive:

- *What legal rights does Paula have regarding confidentiality (e.g., health policies, state law)? Do all families with children who are HIV-positive have these same rights?*
- *If Jeffrey is enrolled in the classroom program, is it ethical for Sherra not to inform Marcia (the classroom teacher) that he is HIV-positive or that there is a child in the classroom who has a communicable disease?*
- *Should Sherra tell her husband Mark that she is working with a child who is HIV-positive?*
- *Who, if anyone, has a need to know about Jeffrey's HIV status?*
- *If Sherra chooses to honor Paula's request to keep Jeffrey's condition a secret, is there anything she should do to protect other people who have contact with him?*
- *Paula seems to think that telling others that Jeffrey is HIV-positive would adversely affect the way that his caregivers interact with him? Is her concern valid?*
- *Should Sherra try to convince Paula that Jeffrey would be better off being cared for at home or that Paula should tell those who may come in contact with Jeffrey (e.g., Paula's parents) that he is HIV-positive?*
- *Is there anyone who Sherra can consult for support and help in decision making without violating Paula's expressed desire for confidentiality?*

Depending on teaching objectives and available time, a final angle of the discussion might delve into the issue of intervention. This discussion might be prompted by questions such as the following:

- *How might Sherra's newfound knowledge that Paula and Jeffrey are HIV-positive affect her priorities in conducting home visits with this family? What might Sherra do to support this family's concerns and priorities?*
- *What additional services or resources (formal and informal) might be useful to Paula and Jeffrey now? How might Sherra explore these resources with Paula?*
- *From which services in your own community could Paula benefit?*
- *What is the future likely to hold for Paula and Jeffrey? What services and supports will they need in the future?*

In extended training activities, using the case story "Daria's Silence" in conjunction with or following "The Need To Know" provides for interesting discussion about the impact of HIV and AIDS on different families and the variations in their needs for service delivery. "Daria's Silence" is a story about an African American teenage mother who lives in the inner city and has minimal resources and questionable family support. Like Paula Goldman, however, both Daria and her infant son Andre are HIV-positive.

Daria's Silence

Topics

Communicating with families, teenage parenting, human immunodeficiency virus (HIV) and acquired immunodeficiency syndrome (AIDS), family support services, cultural diversity, infancy (from birth to age 3 years), low-income families, home-based services, clinic-based services, assessment and diagnosis, medically fragile, confidentiality, extended families

Synopsis

Gayle Daniels has been visiting the Edwards's home in the projects for 7 months now, ever since Daria Edwards left the group home for female juvenile offenders. Daria and her infant son, Andre, are both HIV-positive. Gayle has had a difficult time working with Daria because she always seems angry. There doesn't seem to be a way for Gayle to break through Daria's wall of silence, and any attempts that Gayle makes to develop a trusting relationship with Daria fail miserably. Gayle spends the day accompanying Daria and Andre to the regional pediatric HIV clinic at St. Mark's Hospital. The news regarding Andre is not good, and Gayle is caught off guard when staff members at the clinic take her aside and divulge their concerns about Daria and Andre.

Major Issues

The central issue that this case story addresses is Daria's lack of responsiveness to Gayle's attempts to communicate with her. The majority of recommended practices in early intervention rely on effective parent–professional communication; yet there are parents, such as Daria, who are forced into services that they may not want or who, for other reasons, are not receptive to early intervention professionals. This story serves as a mechanism to explore strategies for working with these types of families. Numerous other issues, the most obvious of which is the issue of HIV and AIDS, are also addressed in this case story. Most important, however, are the issues related to multiple-agency involvement with this family. In particular, the service provider working with Daria must decide how to handle some questionable practices on the part of the hospital clinic staff who also work with Daria and her baby.

Teaching Notes

There are three main issues in this case story that you may choose to introduce. The first issue is that of the relationship between Daria and the home-based service provider, Gayle Daniels. The second potential topic for discussion is what Gayle should do about the events that have taken place during Andre's appointment at St. Mark's HIV clinic. A third issue that the group can discuss is which additional services and supports might be helpful to Daria and Andre now and in the future. Although all three of these issues can be included in the discussion of this story, your teaching objectives and the characteristics of your particular audience will determine the amount of time and depth of coverage for each issue. Be aware that discussions of this case story may require a bit more time than a less complicated case. If your class time is relatively short (e.g., a 1-hour class), you may choose to have the discussion span two class periods.

Because this case story involves numerous people, a good way to start the discussion is to say, *There are a lot of people involved in Daria's life. Let's begin by making a list of them.* As people or agencies are mentioned, write them down on the board or a flipchart. It's a good idea to make several lists, sorting them as you go along. For example, categories for grouping may include family members, St. Mark's clinic staff, early intervention professionals, informal supports (e.g., Vanessa), or other professionals (e.g., local health clinic). You might also ask about people or agencies that were not specifically mentioned in the story but might also be involved in Daria's situation (e.g., probation officer, courts, social services). In fact, this is an excellent case story for developing an eco-map (e.g., à la Brofenbrenner) of the various influences in Daria's life.

In discussing Gayle's difficulty in establishing an effective relationship with Daria, the group should consider how both Gayle and Daria have contributed to their troublesome relationship. You might begin this aspect of the discussion by asking, *What did you think about the way Gayle interacted with Daria?* Audience reactions to this question may surprise you. Some groups are very positive about Gayle's attempts to interact with Daria, whereas other groups can be alarmingly negative, claiming that Gayle acted coldly, defensively, or standoffishly. Whatever the participants' responses are, ask follow-up questions to encourage the expression of alternative viewpoints and to elicit specific details on which the participants' opinions are based. Questions may include, *Was there anything that Gayle did right in her interactions with Daria? Was there anything that you would have done differently if you had been in Gayle's position? Can you give me a specific example of how Gayle behaved (e.g., empowering, respectful, cold, standoffish)?*

To re-direct the discussion to Daria's contributions to her negative relationship with Gayle, you could ask, *Why do you think Daria is so angry?* or, *What would make Daria act the way she does?* Participants' responses to these questions can be very interesting and insightful. If, however, the group offers only a single, simple response such as *Daria's a teenager—all teenagers act like she does,* you will want to encourage them to expound on their response. Depending on participants' comments thus far regarding Gayle's and Daria's relationship, you may want to conclude this aspect of the discussion by saying, *At several points in the story, Gayle questions whether she will ever get through to Daria and if it's even worth trying. What do you think? Is it a waste of Gayle's time for her to continue trying with Daria?* (*Note:* The ethnic or cultural background of service providers is often mentioned by participants during the discussion of the relationship between Gayle and Daria. If desired, you could broach this topic yourself.)

If your teaching objectives include the IFSP process or family-centered practices, you might want to expand the discussion outlined previously into these topics. For example, you might ask, *What does Daria want? What's important to her?* Although Daria doesn't say much in the story, participants often pick up on small aspects of Daria's behavior (e.g., buying the macaroni and cheese for Andre in the hospital cafeteria). Make a list of Daria's priorities and needs on the board. Next, ask participants, *What else do you think Daria might want for herself? For Andre?* and, *If you were Gayle, what additional concerns or priorities would you have for this family? Are these priorities consistent with what you think Daria wants?* You may choose to postpone this part of the discussion until after discussing the clinic visit.

If assessment issues are a part of your teaching agenda, and especially if your audience includes participants who are likely to work in environments similar to St. Mark's, you may want to begin discussion of the clinic visit by asking about the entire program. For example, you might begin by asking, *What did you think of the HIV clinic at St. Mark's Hospital? What do you think it might be like for families to bring their children to hospital clinics such as the one described here?* Participants will most likely bring up issues such as the amount of time that families spend waiting, the staff's lack of interest in what outside professionals have to say, and even the messages sent to the families by the clothing that the professionals in these clinics wear (Donna Friedman's taupe high heels and matching hose are almost always a topic of conversation!). You could then ask the participants if the clinic's environment has to be this way and, if not, how it might be improved.

The most important topic to discuss, however, is the impromptu meeting during which the clinic professionals at St. Mark's disclose to Gayle their concerns about Daria—without Daria's knowledge. First, you may ask, *What concerns did the clinic staff have about Andre and Daria?* and, *Do you think their concerns are justified?* Then, you will want to ask the group, *Was it appropriate for the clinic staff to talk to Gayle without Daria's knowledge? If not, what should they have done instead?* After a brief discussion of the clinic staff's behavior, you may want to move on to discussing Gayle's behavior. You could ask, *Although Gayle didn't know what she was getting into when she first entered the room with the clinic staff, what do you think about how she handled herself in the meeting after she realized what was happening?*

The next big question is, *What should Gayle do next?* Participants should consider whether Gayle should tell Daria about her meeting with the clinic staff, what they said about Daria and Andre, and if Gayle should have any further discussions with the clinic staff. As always, make sure that the students identify several different solutions as well as the pros and cons and potential consequences of each of the identified options. This final line of questioning should include discussion of what Gayle should do during her next visit with Daria as well as what she should do over the next few weeks or months. This conversation may evolve into a discussion of what this family is likely to need in the more distant future and what, if anything, could be done now to prepare for the future. This aspect of the discussion will, of course, address specific issues about HIV and AIDS.

In concluding the discussion of this case story, there are several general topics on which you can choose to focus. You could have the group first talk about other types of families or situations in which it is difficult to form relationships and then develop some general guidelines for handling such situations. You could also address how a service provider might work with other agencies that are not family-friendly. General discussions about working with children or families who are HIV-positive or have AIDS or working with teen parents are also possibilities.

In extended training activities, using the case story "The Need To Know" in conjunction with or following "Daria's Silence" provides for interesting discussion of the various impacts of HIV and AIDS on families and of the variations in their needs for service delivery. "The Need To Know" is a story about a teenage mother from a middle-class family. The young mother's situation is quite different from Daria's, but, like Daria, both she and her son are HIV-positive.

Sunset View

Topics

Domestic violence, personal safety, autism, assessment and diagnosis, infancy (from birth to age 3 years), home-based services, low-income families, professional boundaries, confidentiality

Synopsis

Alice has been growing increasingly suspicious that Miguel, an 18-month-old infant whom she visits weekly, may have autism. She has been intending to discuss her suspicions with Miguel's mother, Carolyn, for several weeks now but hasn't found an appropriate time to introduce her concerns. Carolyn's life seems difficult enough as it is. Alice can't imagine how Carolyn can continue to live with her husband, Eduardo. He constantly orders Carolyn around and belittles her in front of Alice. One day when Alice arrives at the trailer, Carolyn has a black eye—not the first sign that Eduardo physically abuses her.

Major Issues

There are three main issues in this case story, the first of which is domestic violence. Alice, the home visitor, has been an eyewitness to the degrading manner in which Eduardo treats his wife, Carolyn, and there have been signs of physical abuse. The second issue is that of Alice's personal safety. Not only does this family live in a rough neighborhood, but Alice is very uncomfortable around Eduardo. The third major issue concerns Miguel himself. Carolyn seems relatively unaffected by Miguel's developmental delays, but Alice is becoming increasingly concerned and suspects that Miguel may have autism. Alice must decide whether to approach Carolyn with her suspicion.

Teaching Notes

Although this case story is relatively uncomplicated, it presents some difficult issues that professionals who conduct home visits may encounter—issues for which there are no easy answers. With inservice audiences, you may want to begin the discussion by assessing the degree to which participants have experienced similar situations, and, for all audiences, you may want to begin by asking for the participants' viewpoints regarding the issues presented in the story. To introduce these topics, you could ask, *Have you ever been in a situation similar to the one that Alice faces in this story?* or, in the case of audiences with little experience, *Can you envision yourself in this type of situation one day?* Follow up with the question, *What would (or does) it feel like to be in a situation like this?* In all likelihood, your audience will focus on the issue of spousal abuse because this is the most dramatic issue presented in the story. By allowing participants to talk freely about their experiences and feelings related to this issue, you will attain information about their knowledge and skills in this area. You should be prepared with factual information (i.e., a mini-lecture) about spousal abuse so that you can clear up any misconceptions about this topic that may arise.

The next step in facilitating the discussion should be to return to the story itself. Begin discussion by asking the group to outline the various issues in the story that need to be resolved. You might want to make a list of the story's issues on the board or on a flipchart. First, write down the issues that have already been identified by the group. Then, to prompt the generation of additional issues, you might ask something such as, *Eduardo's abuse of Carolyn is certainly one of Alice's biggest concerns in this story. What other problems or concerns does Alice face?* Issues that the group identifies may include Alice's discomfort in being around Eduardo, Alice's concern for her own personal safety in the trailer park, Carolyn's passivity, Carolyn's apparent lack of awareness of Miguel's developmental delays, Alice's suspicions of autism, and Eduardo's lack of involvement in Miguel's care. As long as the major issues are identified, there is no need to push the group into identifying the rest. The other issues will be recognized as the discussion proceeds.

The next step in the case discussion is to have the group resolve, one by one, each of the identified issues. Assuming that the group has focused on the issue of domestic violence during the initial discussion, you should start with that topic. As always, try to steer the group away from identifying solutions before analyzing the situation. To initiate a group analysis of the situation, you can ask a series of questions, including the following:

- *Do you think that Alice has good reason to suspect that Carolyn has been physically abused by Eduardo?*
- *Is spousal abuse an issue in which an early intervention home visitor should become involved?*
- *Should Alice have done anything before now?*
- *Should Alice or Kim (the speech-language therapist) have done anything about their suspicions on the day they arrived at the trailer and saw Carolyn's black eye?*

Next, you can move the group toward identifying solutions. You might ask, *Should Alice (or Kim) act on her suspicions of spousal abuse now? If so, what should she do?* Encourage the group to identify at least several alternatives. If participants don't come up with this idea on their own, you also can encourage them to entertain the possibility of Alice's electing, for the time being, not to do anything at all. In discussing the various solutions, be sure the group considers the potential ramifications of each. These ramifications might include effects that the solution would have on the relationship between Eduardo and Carolyn, on the relationship between Carolyn and Alice, on Carolyn's ability to take care of herself and Miguel, and on services for Miguel (e.g., Eduardo could react by putting an end to home visits). The participants should consider both short- and long-term consequences. If the group decides that Alice should speak with Carolyn about the suspected abuse, you might want to push participants into identifying exactly what Alice should say to Carolyn and how Carolyn might respond to this. (*Note:* At some point during the discussion of spousal abuse, you should probably ask the group whether they think Miguel is at any risk for physical harm in this situation and, if so, how this risk would influence their decisions.)

A similar line of questioning could be used to determine what Alice should do about her suspicions of autism. The discussion would therefore include answering the following questions:

- *Does Alice have just cause for suspecting autism?*
- *Should Alice have acted on her suspicions before now?*
- *Should Alice act on her suspicions now? If so, what are her options?*
- *What are the potential ramifications of each alternative?*

You will need to decide whether to discuss the other issues in this case story (e.g., Alice's concerns for her personal safety, how Alice should cope with Eduardo's lustful stares on home visits, Eduardo's lack of involvement in home visits). This decision should be based on your teaching objectives, time availability, and the concerns expressed by participants throughout the discussion of the case.

Finally, this case story lends itself to a more general discussion of ethics in home visiting, specifically with regard to the issue of professional roles and boundaries. Participants could also address the issue of confidentiality in home-based services. To open this area of discussion, you might begin by saying, *Because Alice provides services in this family's home, she is aware of a great deal more about what goes on in this family than she would be if she were Miguel's classroom teacher or a clinic-based service provider. Does this mean she is responsible for attending to all of the issues she is aware of? Where does a home visitor draw the line?* You could expand the discussion by asking participants about other things they may see or be made aware of while conducting home visits and the degree to which they think a home visitor should be responsible for attending to these things. You might also discuss the issue of confidentiality as it relates to things of which home visitors might be made aware while working. For example, you could ask, *Should Alice really be telling anyone about the interactions she has seen between Eduardo and Carolyn? If so, who else has the right to know?* or, *How do you distinguish between what information obtained during home visits—including observations—you should share with other team members or agencies and what information you should keep confidential?*

A Family Feud

Topics

Consultation, inclusion, child care quality, conflicts within families, family values and priorities, cultural diversity, preschool (ages 3–5 years), classroom- or center-based services, single parenting, working-class families, extended families

Synopsis

Hannah Osborne arrives at the Catesville Community Child Care Center and is told that 3-year-old Conrad Brown no longer attends the center. Shonda Brown, Conrad's mother, took him out of the center at the end of the previous week and enrolled him in another center across town. With Shonda's permission, Hannah makes a visit to the new child care center in Donsbridge. The center appears plush and expensive, but Hannah is alarmed by the new teacher's negative attitude toward children with disabilities. Hannah questions whether Conrad can ever be fully included under such conditions. On a subsequent home visit with Shonda, Hannah becomes aware of the reason that Shonda moved Conrad to the center in Donsbridge. Shonda is furious at her ex-mother-in-law, Louise, and says she no longer wants Louise to be involved in Conrad's life. Hannah wants to support Shonda's decisions, but she is concerned about how the recent changes in Conrad's child care placement will affect Shonda and Conrad. Hannah is also sympathetic to Louise's position and feels that Shonda may be judging Louise too harshly. Should Hannah involve herself in a family feud? And what is really best for Conrad?

Major Issues

The major issue in this case story centers on Hannah's perception that Shonda's priorities and decisions do not appear to be in Conrad's best interest. Because Shonda's decisions included transferring Conrad from a reasonably supportive child care environment to one that is extremely questionable, issues related to the quality of child care for children with disabilities and consultation strategies also arise in this story.

Teaching Notes

As with most case discussions, it is a good idea to begin by identifying the major issues or problems in the situation. You could initiate discussion by posing questions such as, *What are the major issues that Hannah Osborne is facing right now in working with the Brown family?* or, *What decisions must Hannah Osborne make, given the changed circumstances of the Brown family?* This should initiate discussion of at least three major issues:

1. Hannah's concerns about the caregivers' attitudes in Conrad's new child care center and their ability to provide meaningful learning experiences for Conrad
2. Whether Hannah should continue to communicate with Conrad's grandmother Louise
3. The effects of the rift between Shonda and Louise and whether Hannah should involve herself in their disagreement

Rather than complete a list of all the major issues first, it is more than likely that participants will provide their opinions about each of the issues as they are identified. Some participants may be critical of Shonda, proposing that she has been immature in compromising Conrad for the sake of getting back at Louise or her ex-husband, Robert. If these issues do not arise, it may prove useful for you to question the participants about Shonda's reasons for her actions and how the participants feel about these reasons. In questioning the group, different perspectives may be offered. Although you may not specifically address each opinion, hearing the participants' reactions allows you to assess the degree to which the participants are accepting of or judgmental of Shonda's values and priorities.

As is typical in most case discussions, participants will begin to provide solutions to the issues as each issue is introduced. Without being too authoritative, try to steer the group away from doing this. The participants should identify two issues in this case before they begin to discuss solutions:

1. What does Conrad need in terms of the characteristics of child care environments that would be supportive of his development (minimal and ideal situations)?
2. Is Hannah Osborne justified in assuming that Conrad's previous child care center (Catesville Community Child Care Center) is preferable to his new center?

The second question will challenge participants to consider why they are drawn to Maura Desmond's program in Catesville and whether Hannah has been too hasty in her conclusions that the caregivers at the new center won't be able to provide Conrad with the care he needs.

Following the discussion about the quality of child care and Conrad's needs, the group should begin to identify alternative solutions to the various issues that Hannah Osborne faces. Which issues participants should address first or emphasize more will depend on your teaching objectives and your ongoing assessment of the group's learning needs. After the students have offered alternative solutions and have made a decision as to which solution would be best, the group should be encouraged to identify the specific actions that would be necessary to implement their decision. For example, if the group decides that Hannah should share her observations and concerns about the new child care center with Shonda, you could ask the participants questions such as, *What words might Hannah actually use? How might Shonda react? How might Hannah initiate a discussion with Shonda in which they explore the impact of Shonda's recent decisions, including the effect of refusing Louise's support and the effects of enrolling Conrad in the new center in terms of tuition costs and transportation distance?* Suppose the group decides that Hannah should work with the caregivers at the new center to try and make it a better placement for Conrad. *How should Hannah proceed in doing this?*

Throughout or following the discussion of this case, a general discussion of some of the issues may be entertained or prompted. For example, this case lends itself to further discussion of the challenges to inclusion and of effective strategies for specialists whose work involves collaboration with general early childhood personnel. Hannah's awkward position in dealing with Louise's request for information about her grandson might also be extended to explore effective ways of handling situations in which family members disagree or situations involving marital separation and divorce.

chapter 13

Grandpa's Lap

Topics

Parent–professional conflicts, specialized therapies, intervention planning, IEP, IFSP, integrated therapies, multiple and severe disabilities, preschool (ages 3–5 years), classroom- or center-based services, cultural diversity, interdisciplinary coordination, service delivery models, legal guardianship, extended families, communicating with families

Synopsis

Pam Bowman usually speaks with Demitrius's grandmother, who walks Demitrius and his sister to preschool most mornings. The grandmother has always seemed pleased with Demitrius's progress in Pam's classroom. How could Pam have known how unhappy Demitrius's grandfather has been with the services that Demitrius has been receiving? Demitrius has been absent from Pam's classroom for a prolonged period, so Pam makes an unscheduled visit to the grandparents' home to determine what is wrong. When she arrives, Demitrius's grandmother is out on an errand and only Mr. Carey, Demitrius's grandfather, is at home. Mr. Carey is unfriendly toward Pam and, during an awkward conversation, he tells her that he does not want Demitrius to be seen by the physical therapist any more. Apparently, Mr. Carey had witnessed a therapy session at the school and didn't like the fact that the physical therapist had made Demitrius cry. It also sounds as though the grandfather might not want Demitrius to continue to attend Pam's classroom. Who is responsible for what has happened, and who should repair the damage? Pam is very concerned that Demitrius will be taken out of all services and, given the severity of his cerebral palsy and his cognitive delays, Demitrius clearly needs intervention.

Major Issues

This case addresses two major issues, which actually culminate to form the central problem—parental dissatisfaction with services. The first major issue relates to the establishment of effective parent–professional communication and partnerships in center-based programs and handling disagreements when they arise. The second major issue addresses how contracted, specialized therapies are conducted within center-based programs. In this case story, the issue of specialized therapy forms the basis for the grandfather's dissatisfaction with services and for his decision to withdraw his grandson from the program. Although this story specifically addresses the use of contracted physical therapy services, the issues are general enough for the story to be used in discussing any of the specialized therapies or other forms of contractual services for children. Content related to specialized therapies that you may cover in this case discussion includes professional–professional communication, IEP/IFSP development, roles and responsibilities related to working with parents, integrated therapy, role-release, routines-based assessment, and intervention planning.

Teaching Notes

It is probably better to discuss both of the case's major issues together rather than one at a time, as they are interwoven into the sequence of events in the story. As each of these issues arises in the discussion, you can explore it in more detail. You can also conduct a more general discussion of one or both of these issues separately at the conclusion of the decision-making process.

A good place to begin the discussion is to ask the group about the various contributing factors in the situation. For example you might say, *Pam has unexpectedly encountered a rather sticky situation with Demitrius's grandfather. Before deciding what Pam should do next, let's take a minute to go back to the beginning. What do you think caused this problem in the first place?* As the participants begin to identify the contributing factors, list their suggestions on the board or on a flipchart. If responses start to dwindle before the group has recognized all the important factors, prompt the participants for additional suggestions by asking, *Could anything have been done differently that may have prevented the situation from arising in the first place?* You may also be able to elicit additional contributing factors by ensuring that the group attends to the actions (or lack of action) of each of the various players in the situation. For example, if the group restricts their comments to what Lori Skidmore (the physical therapist) has or hasn't done, you might ask, *What about Demitrius's teacher, Pam? Is she in any way responsible for what has happened? Could she have done anything to prevent the situation?* This line of questioning should introduce a number of topics that the group can refer to again when the discussion moves into identifying solutions (see "Topics" listed previously).

Adhering to the events that have already occurred in the story, you then could ask, *Do you think Pam made the right decision in going to Demitrius's grandparents' house after school?* This could be followed by a variety of questions, such as, *Was it really Pam's responsibility to talk to the grandparents? Should Pam have done something other than make an unannounced home visit? Should Lori have contacted the grandparents instead? What do you think would have happened if Lori had gone to Demitrius's grandparents' house?* If your teaching objectives include communication skills, you might also ask, *What did you think about the way Pam conducted herself in her interactions with Mr. Carey? Should she have done anything differently? Should she have done or said anything else before leaving the Careys' house?*

To initiate a discussion of this situation's potential solutions, you could say, *So far we've talked a lot about what caused the problems in this story and what might have been done differently to prevent the problems from arising in the first place. In the story, however, these things weren't done. Let's look at the situation as it exists. What choices does Pam have now for repairing the damage that has been done?* Make a list on the board or on a flipchart as the participants identify the various options. You can ask the group to discuss the pros and cons of each option as the options are mentioned, or you can wait until a number of options are listed and then have the group discuss the benefits and drawbacks of each as they attempt to choose the best course of action.

In this case story, there are actually two professionals who have potential responsibility for handling the situation: Pam and Lori. However, because at the end of the story the ball has been left in Pam's court, it is likely that the group will gear the solutions toward what Pam should do next. Therefore, at some point, you may want to ask whether Pam should tell Lori what happened on her visit to the Careys' and what responsibility, if any, Lori should have in resolving the situation. Finally, if participants don't bring up the topic of Demitrius's mother while identifying solutions, you may want to remind them of her potential role by asking, *At one point in the story, Lori Skidmore wanted to contact Demitrius's mother. Is this a viable alternative?* Depending on your teaching objectives and time constraints, you may want to broach the issue of legal guardianship in this story.

Remember, too, that Mr. Carey's message remains unclear to Pam at the close of the story. She isn't certain whether the grandfather wants to discontinue all services or just Lori's physical therapy. Therefore, the group must first consider how to determine the activities in which Demitrius's grandfather (and grandmother) will and won't allow Demitrius to participate. Then, the group must consider solutions based on the various decisions the grandfather might make. Thus, while identifying solutions, you will want to ask the group, *What should Pam do if Mr. Carey decides that he doesn't want* any *services for Demitrius?* and, *What should Pam (and Lori) do if Mr. Carey allows Demitrius to return to the classroom, but not to physical therapy with Lori?* In discussing both of these possibilities, you may have good cause to ask, *What is it that Demitrius really needs? What would happen if he didn't get these things?* If necessary, refer the group to Demitrius's IEP that is presented as a supplement to this story and that provides an implicit description of Demitrius's disabilities and skill levels.

This case lends itself to more general discussion of several topics, the most obvious of which are the use of contracted specialized therapies in classroom-based programs and home–school communication and parent–professional partnerships in classroom-based programs. With regard to specialized therapies, you could ask the group what teachers, therapists, and program administrators can do to ensure that they provide the most effective services to children and their families. This might involve discussion of how therapists should use their time, how therapists should coordinate therapy with classroom activities, the therapists' participation in IEP/IFSP development, and the therapists' roles in communicating with families.

There are several activities or assignments that you could choose to conduct in conjunction with this case story. For example, you could ask individuals or groups to rewrite Demitrius's IEP so that it

- Reflects an integrated therapy or transdisciplinary model of service delivery
- Is more meaningful to the family and/or reflects a family-centered approach
- Reflects a routines-based approach to intervention planning
- Incorporates a combination of any of the preceding suggestions

A related activity would be to break the audience into small groups and have each group develop a brief written policy outlining how contractual services would be used if they were in charge of a center-based program for preschoolers. The policy should include a listing of the roles and responsibilities for all of the specialized therapists (physical, occupational, speech-language) who work for the program. When discussing the groups' written policies, you might ask how therapists are likely to respond (i.e., Would anyone work for them?) and what complications they could encounter (e.g., legal issues, conflicts with professional standards).

Silent Partner

Topics

Parent–professional conflicts, classroom- or center-based services, values, classroom policies, preschool (ages 3–5 years), speech-language delays, low-income families

Synopsis

Roz Polikanski is perpetually late in picking up her daughter Amy from the preschool Amy attends for children with special needs. Samantha Price, Amy's teacher, is somewhat irritated by Roz's tardiness but is more concerned about the overall quality of home life that Roz provides for 3-year-old Amy. Samantha's concerns about Amy's home life are based largely on suspicion. For example, Samantha questions the numerous "uncles" who arrive with Roz when Roz comes to pick up Amy at the end of the day. This day a new suspicion arises—one that Samantha finds difficult to ignore. Some money is missing from Samantha's desk, and she strongly suspects that Roz Polikanski has taken it.

Major Issues

Although the issues in this case story are not too dramatic, they do represent common challenges that teachers face in providing classroom-based preschool services, whether the services are in general child care settings or in classroom programs specifically designated for preschoolers with special needs. First, Roz's persistent tardiness in picking up Amy from preschool is a classic complaint of preschool teachers, one that often provokes a more emotional response than might seem justified. Some teachers perceive this as an indication that the preschooler's parents do not respect them. Second, Samantha's concern about the quality of Roz's parenting (i.e., the stream of men coming and going in her life, not following through on activities to facilitate Amy's speech) introduces numerous questions about parental involvement and the role of the classroom teacher: *What are the boundaries of "good parenting"? To what extent can teachers expect parents to follow through with therapy at home?* and, *What is the role of the classroom teacher in terms of his or her responsibility for knowing what goes on in the children's homes and for intervening in family issues?* Third, the issue of the stolen money represents the last straw for Samantha. Is the stolen money really as big of an issue as Samantha perceives it to be?

Teaching Notes

You may want to begin the discussion of this case story by assessing audience reactions to the problems Samantha Price faces in working with Roz Polikanski. What are the participants' opinions about the issues this case presents? With inservice audiences you may want to identify similar incidents that they have encountered while working with the families of children in their own classrooms. To identify these incidents, you could begin by asking, *What do you think about the problems Samantha faces in working with Amy's mother? Have you ever experienced these kinds of problems in your classroom? Are there other problems that you've had with parents?* Write down the problems participants identify, as you may want to re-visit these issues at the conclusion of the case discussion. For less experienced audiences, you should probably stick with the problems the case story presents. Thus, you could begin by asking, *What do you think about the problems Samantha is having with Amy's mother?*

For all audiences, the next step should be to identify the problems. You could ask, *What are Samantha Price's concerns about Amy and Roz Polikanski? Let's make a list.* As participants begin to identify problems and concerns, make a list on the board or a flipchart. If participants neglect any of the concerns that the story addresses (e.g., Samantha's suspicion that Roz doesn't follow through at home with speech-language activities), be sure to introduce these issues yourself. As the participants identify the problems, ask them to determine the extent to which each problem is a valid concern. If necessary, you can prompt the audience with a series of questions: *How big of a problem is this? Why is it a problem? Who is it a problem for? What may happen if Samantha doesn't deal with this problem?* These questions are likely to prompt a discussion of how to determine when parent–professional conflicts are based on issues of right versus wrong and when they are a result of variances in cultural or personal beliefs. (*Note:* You may want to postpone discussion of the stolen money until after the other issues are addressed, as this issue may be a "hotter" topic.)

After the participants have identified all of the problems and have determined whether each issue merits action on Samantha's part, the next step is to have the group begin to generate potential solutions. Be sure to encourage alternative solutions and to have the group consider the possible consequences of implementing each solution (e.g., Roz's possible reactions) before settling on one. If any of the solutions the participants choose involve talking with Roz, you might want to ask them to specify exactly how they would go about doing this: What words would the participants actually use, and where would they choose to confront Roz?

With experienced audiences, you might want to conclude the discussion by returning to the list of issues they have encountered while working with parents in their own programs. You could ask if, after discussing this case story, they have any further thoughts about these issues or about how they might handle these issues in the future.

Recipe for Rachel

Topics

Parent–professional conflicts, Prader-Willi syndrome, family-centered practices, intervention planning, classroom- or center-based services, preschool (ages 3–5 years), teamwork, communicating with families, inclusion, interprofessional conflicts, supervision

Synopsis

Gwen Roland, a teacher in an inclusive preschool environment, is confused about how to handle a situation concerning 3-year-old Rachel Stevens. Rachel has Prader-Willi syndrome, the most prominent characteristic of which is life-threatening obesity in early adulthood. Rachel's mother, Sandy Stevens, is determined to control her daughter's diet before any real problems begin. Although Gwen agrees with Sandy about the need to control Rachel's diet, she has found it to be far more difficult than she first imagined. It seems that there are always cookies, cakes, and other high-calorie foods in the preschool classroom. Gwen's attempts to control the availability of such foods have been met with resistance from the parents of other children in the classroom, and Gwen's assistant Andrea has sabotaged Gwen's efforts to control what and how much Rachel eats at school. Lately, Gwen has begun to wonder if Sandy is being too strict with Rachel, and the child's recent display of temper tantrums over food have made Gwen even more doubtful about Sandy's approach in dealing with Rachel.

Major Issues

This case story addresses two major issues, both of which are related to implementing family-centered practices within classroom-based preschool programs. The first issue concerns attending to family priorities and honoring parents' requests in a classroom program. In this case story, there are at least three factors that complicate Gwen's ability to honor Sandy's requests:

1. Other staff members are critical of Sandy and strongly disagree with the approach she is taking with Rachel.
2. The parents of the other children in the classroom are not supportive of the changes needed to incorporate Rachel.
3. Gwen herself is beginning to question the appropriateness of Sandy's requests and the manner in which Sandy disciplines Rachel.

The second major issue addresses the role of the teacher in attending to broader family issues. This issue raises concerns about the teacher's available time to attend to family matters as well as issues regarding communication strategies for understanding family priorities and working out parent–professional disagreements.

Teaching Notes

During the first phase of the case discussion, you should ask the group to identify the problem(s) in the situation and the various factors that contribute to the problem(s). You might begin by asking one or several broad questions in order to assess which aspects of the story have affected the participants. For example, you might open with, *What do you think about the situation Gwen faces in working with Rachel Stevens and her mother Sandy?* With inservice or experienced preservice audiences, you might also ask, *Have you ever encountered similar situations in your own work? What was that like for you? Can you identify with how Gwen is feeling?* (*Note:* Participants often will talk about parents' requests to make changes in the classroom to accommodate their religious preferences or the special health needs of their children.) After a brief discussion of the participants' personal experiences, you should re-focus the discussion on the particulars of this case story.

You may want to ask for the participants' perceptions of Sandy and Gwen at the beginning of the discussion if these perceptions have not already been voiced. You can ask, *What is Sandy Stevens like? What words would you use to characterize her?* It's probably best, at this point, not to challenge the participants' perceptions. Make a list of the words that the group uses to describe Sandy on the board or flipchart. This list will be especially important if you intend to use "At the Close of the Day" (Sandy's story) in conjunction with this story, in that you can ask the participants if they have changed their perceptions of Sandy after the role play. With regard to the group's perceptions of Gwen, you can ask, *What kind of a teacher do you think Gwen is? Did you like her style of interacting with the children? With the parents?* (*Note:* Difficulties related to who is in control of the children when parents and teachers are both in the classroom are usually discussed [e.g., Alicia's crying, Rachel and the cupcakes, Sandy's discipline of Rachel at the snack table, Gwen not asking Sandy to help in the classroom as often].) Reactions to Gwen can vary widely across groups.

At this point in the discussion, participants probably will have identified several factors that may have contributed to the problem(s) in the story. You now should ask the group to consider additional contributing factors. If you have kept a running list of these factors on the board or flipchart, you can continue this list as the participants identify additional factors. If not, you may have to back up and write down those factors that the group has already mentioned. To encourage the group to identify other contributing factors, you could say, *In the story, Gwen seems to want to support Sandy's requests and desires related to Rachel, but she's having some difficulties. What's keeping Gwen from doing what Sandy wants?* The group will most likely identify and discuss factors within three major areas:

1. The lack of support from other staff members (e.g., Andrea, Laura, cafeteria staff)
2. The lack of cooperation from the parents of the other children in Gwen's classroom
3. Gwen's own doubts about the appropriateness of Sandy's approach to intervening with Rachel

With regard to this third area, you might want to ask the group, *Is Sandy being too strict with Rachel? What do you think? What would be the best approach to take with Rachel?* If, by chance, the group doesn't address all three of these areas on their own, you may need to prompt them with a few questions. (*Note:* If the group hasn't had experience with Prader-Willi syndrome, they are likely to ask questions about it. Because one premise of the story is that Rachel's mother knows more about the syndrome than Gwen does, you should try to avoid providing too much detail in answering their questions, especially if you plan to follow up with the role-play using "At the Close of the Day.")

The next phase of the discussion should be to identify solutions. To make the transition to this phase, you could begin by summarizing the discussion so far (i.e., the problems and contributing factors). For example, you could say, *Before we decide what Gwen should do next, let's take a minute to review what we've talked about so far.* In the interest of time and to avoid too much repetition, you will probably want to provide this summary yourself and keep it brief. The next step should be to have the group develop a list of the concerns Gwen has about Rachel and Sandy—those things that Gwen must make decisions about. You could say something such as, *At the end of the story, Gwen makes a list of the concerns she has about Rachel and Sandy. What are these concerns?* Write down the concerns as they are identified by the participants. You could also choose to prepare a list ahead of time yourself (i.e., copy items from Gwen's list onto flipchart paper) and then review the list for the group. If you decide to prepare the list in advance, ask the participants, *Are all of these concerns valid? Would you have any additional concerns about Rachel or her family?* Add any additional concerns to the list.

If you are interested in having the group discuss the classroom teacher's role as it relates to broader family-level issues, you might also ask, *Is it appropriate for Gwen to involve herself in all of these issues (refer to the list of concerns)? For which of these issues is Gwen* really *responsible? Are there any issues in which you think Gwen has no business getting involved?* You could also ask the group to identify which of the listed concerns they think are the most critical to address; however, you could also postpone this until later in the discussion.

The first decision that the group needs to make is whether Gwen's intended meeting with Sandy is a good idea. You can ask, *In order to begin addressing her concerns, Gwen has decided to ask Sandy Stevens to meet with her on the premise of updating Gwen's intervention plan for Rachel. Is this a good idea? If not, what would you do?* Although the group may not agree with the premise of the meeting, most participants will agree that Gwen should talk to Sandy. Once this has been decided, you can ask, *If you were Gwen, what would you want to accomplish by talking to Sandy? What would you hope would be the outcome of the meeting?* At this point in the discussion, you could choose to conduct a role play in which the participants assume the roles of Gwen and Sandy, pair up, and conduct the proposed meeting between the two (See "At the Close of the Day: Suggested Activities," pp. 74–77). I strongly recommend this role-play if your teaching objectives include identifying family priorities, understanding family perspectives, developing communication skills in working with families, or facilitating parent–professional partnerships.

If you do not intend to use "At the Close of the Day," you could ask the group to look at the list of concerns about Rachel and Sandy and identify the concerns that are most important for Gwen to address in her meeting with Sandy. Then ask the participants to identify alternative solutions and choose from among the alternatives. As solutions are recognized, the participants will probably detect other issues that can be discussed, such as how to deal with Andrea's and Laura's criticism of Sandy or strategies for dealing with the possible reactions of other parents.

Happy Birthday!

Topics

Preschool transitions, inclusion, behavior problems, service coordination, policy, home-based services, consultation, extended families, speech-language delays

Synopsis

Sachi Daugherty is confused about her grandson James's transition from the infant/toddler (birth to age 3) program to the preschool program sponsored by the public schools. Allison, who works for the infant/toddler program, currently provides home visits; but, her services will end shortly. Allison has been planning James's transition with Sachi for several months, but a number of un-expected developments have occurred over the past few weeks. First, Allison has found out that James cannot continue to receive speech-language therapy at Loving Arms, the child care cen-ter he currently attends, because the center is physically outside the boundaries of the school dis-trict. Second, James's aggressive behavior toward other children at Loving Arms has been a growing concern for the child care staff. Allison has less than 2 months to address these two issues and finalize the transition plan for James. Beyond these immediate concerns, Allison also worries about James's future and the support that might or might not be available to help Sachi care for her grandson in the years ahead.

Major Issues

The first major issue this case story addresses is James's transition from the birth-to-3 services that Allison's program provides to the preschool services that the public school system will provide. This issue raises questions about systems-level policies in the structure of early intervention ser-vices (i.e., seamless system *versus* a change in agency responsibility for services at age 3). It also raises questions about interagency coordination in terms of what Allison can do to influence the receiving agency and make James's transition a success. The second major issue this case story ad-dresses is James's inclusion in regular child care and the difficulties that have arisen as a result of James's aggression in that environment. The third major issue is parent–professional partnerships. Allison must decide whether to withhold hurtful information from Sachi regarding James's ag-gressive behavior, and she must determine the extent to which she should handle the situation with the public school herself rather than encourage Sachi to take action. Allison also must decide how she can help Sachi better handle James at home. Finally, this story raises the issues of how to say "good-bye" to families and how to know when we, as service providers, have done all that we can to prepare the child and his family for the future.

Teaching Notes

During the first phase of the case discussion, participants should identify the problems that Allison is facing in the story and the factors that have contributed to each issue. You can begin this discussion with a broad question such as, *What did you think about Allison's situation in this story?* or you could be more specific by asking, *What are the major problems that Allison has encountered in working with James and his family?* Whichever way you choose to initiate the discussion, you will want to encourage the group to identify at least the following three major issues:

1. Difficulties in securing related services (speech-language therapy) in James's current child care environment following his transition into preschool services
2. Serena Culbreth's decision to move James out of Mary's room and Serena's threat to expel James if his aggression worsens
3. Sachi's difficulties in controlling James's aggressive behavior at home.

The second and third issues could be subsumed under the larger topic of James's aggression; however, you will probably want to broach the issues separately when the group begins to identify solutions.

As the group identifies the story's major issues, write their suggestions on the board or flipchart. Leave enough space under each suggestion to write down the corresponding contributing factors. All three issues need not be identified before beginning to discuss each individual issue in more detail. See where the group takes the discussion and determine for yourself when it is appropriate to move on to identifying the next problem. Do your best, however, to dissuade participants from identifying solutions during this phase of the discussion.

For each of the three major issues, ask the group to discuss how well they think Allison has handled the situation so far and to identify factors that might have contributed to the problem. For example, with regard to the transition issue you might ask, *There are only 2 months left before James makes the transition to the public school system. Should Allison have known about the policy related to school district boundaries and speech-language therapy before this? Was Allison right to have told Sachi Daugherty about this during her home visit? Should she have done anything else before telling Sachi?* You might also discuss the contributing factors at the systems level by asking, *Is there a similar division of agency responsibility for services (i.e., transition) at age 3 in your state or community? How does this type of service structure affect children and families? Why would a state or community choose to have a divided early intervention system? Are there any benefits to a divided system? What safeguards are in place to buffer the negative impacts of transition at age 3?* (See also Discussion Questions #17 and #18 at the end of the case story.) If your main teaching objectives include systems-level issues in transition (i.e., policy and service structure), you may want to postpone detailed discussion of this topic until after the conclusion of the case discussion.

In exploring the contributing factors to the problem of James's aggression, you will want participants to consider both the issues at the child care center and the issues at home. With regard to child care, you could ask, *How do you think Allison handled the conversation with Serena Culbreth, the child care center director? Is Serena Culbreth justified in the position she has taken regarding James's aggression? When talking with Serena, should Allison have done more to advocate for James to stay in Mary's room?* At this point, you might also ask, *Allison chose not to tell Sachi that Serena's real reason for insisting that James be moved out of Mary's room is James's aggression. Why didn't Allison tell Sachi? Should she have?*

In exploring the problem of James's aggression at home, you might want to begin by discussing Allison's overall approach to her work with Sachi Daugherty. For example, you could ask, *What did you think about Allison's style of interacting with Sachi and the other members of the Daugherty household during her home visit?* Then you could focus on James's aggression and other specific aspects of the visit by asking questions such as, *Should Allison have said something to Sachi about how to handle James when he hit his cousin, Missy? Should Allison be doing more during her home visits to include James's grandfather Curt Daugherty? Was it right for Allison to dissuade Sachi from going to the public school to complain about the speech-language therapy issue? Didn't Allison also discourage Sachi from talking to Serena Culbreth about keeping James in Mary's room?*

If your teaching content includes parent–professional partnerships, family-centered practices, or home visiting strategies, you might want to delve even more deeply into the events that transpired during the home visit and into Allison and Sachi's relationship. You could initiate this part of the discussion by asking participants what they liked and didn't like about the way Allison interacted with Sachi during the home visit. You could also ask questions such as, *Do you think Sachi likes and trusts Allison? How can you tell?* and, *Do you think Allison likes and appreciates Sachi? Has she always?* Questions such as these can bring up some interesting issues. For example, participants often comment about Sachi's giving sushi to Allison as Allison is leaving, what this means, and whether it was important for Allison to accept the gift. The participants could also discuss the consequences of Allison's initial complaints about Sachi and the consequences of Allison's negative talk to her teammates about Sachi. The potential influence of Sachi's ethnic and cultural background may also be brought out through such questioning.

At this point, it may be a good idea to summarize the major issues that the participants have broached during their discussion of the case story's problems and contributing factors. Then the group can begin to identify solutions. You could initiate the identification of solutions by asking, *So, what do you think Allison should do next? What choices does she have for handling this situation?* If, however, you are short on time, or if you have specific topics in the story that you want to ensure that the participants address in this phase of the discussion, you could be more directive in your questioning: *Let's first look at the issue of (e.g., James's transition, James's aggression). How do you think Allison should handle this?* As always, make sure the participants generate a sufficient number of alternatives and discuss the pros and cons of each option before they decide on a course of action.

Following a discussion of the immediate decisions that Allison needs to make in this situation, you might want to extend the discussion to talk about the Daugherty family's future. You could begin with, *In this story, Allison seems somewhat saddened to end her relationship with the family. Although she may follow up with the family for a time after James's transition, eventually she will have to stop seeing the Daughertys. What do you think it would be like to say "good-bye" to a family that you have been working with for a long time? What do you think it's like for families when they have to say "good-bye" to you? Are these feelings inevitable? How long should Allison stay involved with this family?* Then you could ask, *What do you think the future will be like for the Daughertys? What will they be likely to need, and are such things typically available in communities? Are these things available in your own community? Is there anything that Allison can do over the next few months to better prepare the Daughertys for the future?*

An Uncertain Future

Topics

Referrals, initial home visits, assessment and diagnosis, vision impairment, health impairments, medically fragile, communicating with families, premature birth, infancy (from birth to age 3 years), interagency coordination, interdisciplinary coordination, home-based services

Synopsis

Shannon Eason was born at 23 weeks' gestation, weighing only 1 pound, 7 ounces, and spent 5 months in the neonatal intensive care nursery before going home. Shannon is now 13 months old and has extensive medical needs and developmental delays. She also has a visual impairment. Recently, Shannon's family, including Shannon, her parents, and her two older siblings, has moved to a new town. Shannon has been evaluated by a vision specialist who, in turn, has referred her to the early intervention program for additional testing and services. Beth Mason received the referral. Beth and Lloyd Farmington, the early intervention program's occupational therapist, make an initial home visit to the Eason's. Although Beth is somewhat intimidated by Shannon's medical history, the thing that really makes her uncomfortable about working with this baby is Shannon's visual impairment. Beth hasn't been specifically trained to work with children who have sensory impairments. The visit to the Eason's home reveals that Shannon has significant cognitive and motor delays, but Beth is uncertain about what percentage of Shannon's delays can be attributed to her premature birth. Beth is also unsure about how to figure in the effects of Shannon's vision impairment. However, the most pressing issue at the moment is what Beth should say to Shannon's mother, who obviously expects some answers to her questions.

Major Issues

The major issue this case story addresses is how a service provider can effectively handle initial contacts with children and their families, including how the service provider should use any information provided by other professionals, interpret assessment results, make preliminary diagnoses and prognoses, share assessment results with parents, and begin the process of determining appropriate services and interventions. In this story, the child is a premature baby who has multiple health impairments, cognitive and motor delays, and a significant vision impairment.

Teaching Notes

This case story addresses two very difficult assessment issues. First, how does a service provider determine the influence of extreme prematurity and associated health impairments in making preliminary diagnoses and prognoses, and, second, how does the service provider determine the extent to which sensory impairments may influence progress across the various developmental domains? The first of these issues is particularly important in early intervention work, as it is a fairly common characteristic of children receiving services.

There are three major areas of discussion you should introduce when using this case story:

1. Child assessment and diagnosis
2. Sharing assessment results with parents
3. The preliminary determination of needed services and interventions

The characteristics of your audience and your teaching objectives will determine the order in which you introduce these issues and the depth of the ensuing discussion. For example, if you are using the case with an interdisciplinary inservice audience, you may want to go into great detail while discussing Shannon's diagnosis and prognosis. In contrast, preservice audiences may not have sufficient knowledge or experience to explore this issue at nearly the same depth. This is not to say that preservice audiences can't benefit from this aspect of the discussion. In fact, this case story is an excellent vehicle for increasing their awareness of the knowledge base and potential contributions of the various disciplines involved in early intervention and for developing an understanding of the medical complications and developmental impacts frequently associated with extreme prematurity (e.g., bilirubin and phototherapy, bronchopulmonary dysplasia [BPD], gastrostomy, intraventricular hemorrhage, patent ductus arteriosis [PDA]). Be sure, however, that you are knowledgeable about these issues, as you may be counted on to provide explanations.

With regard to the issues of assessment, diagnosis, and prognosis, you could begin the discussion by asking about Shannon's etiology: *What do we know about Shannon's history that may account, at least in part, for her current developmental delays?* For each contributing factor the group identifies, you may want to ask, *How might this be influencing Shannon's current level of development?* and, *To what extent is it likely to continue to influence her development? For how long?* You could also ask, *Is there any other information that you would want to have that the reports Beth received from other agencies did not provide? How would this information help you?*

Next, you can address the issue of Shannon's current developmental status by posing a series of questions: *Based on Shannon's history, Virginia Cousins's vision assessment, Beth's and Lloyd's observations during their initial home visit, and Lloyd's occupational therapy assessment report, what would you conclude about Shannon's development? What would be your preliminary diagnoses? How certain do you feel about this? What additional testing, if any, would you want to have done?* As conclusions about Shannon's developmental status and diagnosis are offered, keep a running list on the board or flipchart. Afterward, you might also want to ask the group what their greatest concerns are regarding Shannon's development. In other words, what would they consider priorities for intervention? You could place an asterisk beside those items on the board that the participants identify as their highest priorities.

Finally, you might want to ask the group for their prediction about Shannon's future development: *What do you think Shannon will be like when she is 3 years old? 5 years old? How certain do you feel about your predictions?* (*Note:* An alternative strategy would be to assign participants to small groups and have each group answer these questions on their own. Then reconvene the large group and ask a representative from each small group to report their conclusions. If you choose this option, make certain that your instructions are very clearly written out.)

At an appropriate point in the conversation, perhaps when participants reveal uncertainty about the degree of Shannon's delays that are attributable to prematurity or vision impairment, you may want to begin discussion of the affective aspects of this issue. For example, you might say, *In this story, Beth feels uncomfortable about working with Shannon because of Shannon's vision impairment. Beth is also uncomfortable when Shannon's mother asks whether Shannon's speech delays might be attributable to the fact that Shannon was on a respirator for 4 months. How comfortable would you feel if you were suddenly asked to take responsibility for providing home-based services to Shannon Eason? Have you ever been in situations with children during which you felt uncertain about your knowledge or skills? How should a service provider handle such situations?*

To make the transition from talking about Shannon to talking about Shannon's family, you could summarize the participants' opinions about Shannon's current level of functioning, as well as their diagnoses, prognoses, and concerns, and then ask, *So, if you were in Beth Mason's shoes, what would you tell Shannon's mother, Kaye?* You also could have the group decide on the exact words that Beth should use when speaking to Kaye. Finally, you could ask the group to discuss the ethics of withholding or limiting information or opinions in their conversation with Kaye.

To continue the discussion about the family, you could ask participants how they felt about the manner in which Beth Mason and Lloyd Farmington conducted their initial visit to the Easons'. What did the participants like about this first visit? What, if anything, would they have done differently? How would they have concluded this first home visit? Next, you might want to ask the group, *What do you think this home visit was like for Kaye Eason?* And, more generally, *What do you think life with Shannon is like for Kaye Eason? What might she be feeling? What worries might she have, and what questions might she want answered? What would probably be most helpful to Kaye right now?* You may want to write brief notes on the board or flipchart reflecting the group's responses to these questions, especially if you plan on using the companion story, "What Color Is Forever?," which provides Kaye Eason's perspective.

In this case story, a discussion of the services and interventions that might be of help to the Easons is optional. This issue can be introduced at the end of discussions about assessment and diagnosis or, here, following a discussion of the family. You could ask, *What disciplines or agencies should be involved in intervention planning for this child and family? What types of services are likely to be needed by Shannon and her family?* and, *What model of service delivery would probably be best (e.g., transdisciplinary, interdisciplinary, multidisciplinary)?* You could ask the group further questions about interagency and interdisciplinary coordination, who should be responsible for service coordination, and how it can best be accomplished. When working with an inservice audience, you could also ask the participants what types of services would be available in their own communities (including fees, eligibility, and hours of operation), how services are coordinated, and the impact of these services on families.

You should consider following this case discussion with a discussion of the supplemental case story, "What Color Is Forever?," and its suggested teaching activities if your teaching objectives include family-centered practices; identifying family concerns, priorities, and resources; understanding parent perspectives; or parent–professional communication.

cc: Parker Ellis

Topics

Kindergarten transitions, interprofessional conflicts, inclusion, supervision, mental retardation, preschool (ages 3–5 years), behavior problems, middle- to upper-income families

Synopsis

Dana Tolliver has worked hard to ensure a smooth transition to kindergarten for Lucas Coleman. Frequently during the past 3 months, Dana has discussed Lucas's needs with Yolanda Powell, an employee of the Clarksburg City School system who handles all of the transitions for children entering public school. Lucas Coleman has Down syndrome and has been served by the Lochridge Children's Center's various early intervention programs since he was 6 weeks old. Dana works at Lochridge Center and has been Lucas's service coordinator for the past 2 years—ever since Lucas left Lochridge's toddler classroom to attend a regular child care center in the community. Although there have been a few problems with Lucas's inclusion in regular child care, overall he has done quite well, and his parents want him to attend a regular kindergarten classroom next year.

Lucas's kindergarten transition is proceeding as planned until 2 days before Lucas's placement committee meeting, when Yolanda Powell calls Dana to tell her that the committee is unlikely to approve an inclusive placement for Lucas. Yolanda's predictions turn out to be true. Even worse, Lynette Williams, the chairperson of the school placement committee, treats Lucas's parents insensitively during the meeting. Angered at Lynette's behavior, Dana speaks up on behalf of Lucas's parents and reminds them of their rights to appeal the decision. Dana's behavior, however, is not without consequence. The chairperson quickly inflicts her revenge, and Dana finds herself being offered up as a political sacrifice by the administrators at Lochridge Children's Center.

Major Issues

This case story's major issue is the transition of a child with Down syndrome into kindergarten. More specifically, this case addresses the issue of transition when the receiving agency is not family friendly or receptive to the idea of full inclusion. A second issue in this story is the absence of support for recommended practices within the service provider's own agency. In this instance, the lack of support from administrators appears to be prompted by interagency politics.

Teaching Notes

This case is especially effective when your teaching objectives focus on the topic of transitions because it demonstrates that, sometimes, despite a practitioner's best efforts to engage in exemplary transition-planning practices, the transition may still go wrong. And when the transition does go wrong, practitioners are left to make some difficult decisions on their own.

The discussion questions following this case story provide a good outline for facilitating the case discussion. Because this case involves a number of characters from different agencies, it might be helpful to begin by having the participants identify the case's various characters, as well as the agencies for which these characters work and their roles within these agencies. You should keep a running list of the various characters as the participants identify them, perhaps grouping the characters according to the agencies with which they are associated.

After the various characters have been identified, you should initiate a discussion of what has already happened in the story. This discussion could be prompted by a series of leading questions about the actions and possible motives of the various characters in the story. Because the story is told from Dana Tolliver's perspective, you should probably begin the discussion with her. First, you can encourage discussion about her efforts in planning Lucas's transition by asking, *Did Dana do everything she could to ensure a smooth transition and to get the placement that the Colemans wanted for Lucas? If not, what else could she have done?* Or you could ask, *In retrospect, is there anything Dana could have done to prevent any of the unpleasant events that have occurred in this situation?*

Next, you could prompt the participants to discuss the meeting with the school placement committee. This discussion could include questions about how Dana prepared the Coleman family: *Did Dana Tolliver inadvertently set up the Colemans to be hurt? Could Dana have done more to prepare Lucas's parents for the meeting?* This phase of the discussion should also include questions about Dana's behavior during the actual meeting: *What did you think about the way that Dana conducted herself during Lucas's placement and IEP meeting with the school system? Was Lynette Williams's criticism of Dana's behavior during the meeting justified? Should Dana have done more to advocate for the family during the meeting?*

Finally, you could have participants discuss Dana's behavior after the meeting: *Should Dana have done anything after the meeting? Should she have spoken more with Lucas's parents in the parking lot . . . . Should she have tried to address the situation during the 3 days that passed between the placement meeting and when she was called onto the carpet by Glen Atwater?*

The participants' responses to questions about Dana's behavior most likely will be varied, ranging from full sympathy for Dana and feeling as though Dana did everything right to strong criticism of Dana, especially regarding the way she handled herself in the meeting. It is difficult, if not impossible, to predict which direction a particular group may take. If participants' reactions are strongly biased in one direction, it might be worth playing a subtle "devil's advocate" to try to obtain another perspective.

The questions outlined above will obviously pinpoint some of the contributing factors to the problems in this case. To identify the rest of the factors, you could ask participants for their perspectives on the actions of the other characters in the story. Most important, what did the group think of the way that Glen Atwater, Lynette Williams, and Yolanda Powell conducted themselves in this situation? Why might they have behaved in the way that they did? It is particularly interesting to hear participants' various opinions regarding Lynette Williams's possible motives.

Prior to identifying possible solutions, it might be useful to ask the group, *What is really best for Lucas?* More often than not, participants will favor full inclusion for Lucas without considering the potential drawbacks. Depending on your teaching objectives, you may want to spend some time having the group explore the possible benefits and drawbacks to the various placement options for Lucas. If, by chance, participants are adamant about the option of full inclusion for Lucas, you may want to prompt them to consider other alternatives by asking questions such as, *Dana sneered at Yolanda Powell's compromise of partial inclusion at Sandalwood Elementary School. Is partial inclusion really such a bad idea? Wouldn't Lucas get more therapy at Sandalwood? Wouldn't he get more individualized instruction from better-qualified teachers?*

In making the transition from analyzing the situation to identifying solutions, it may be helpful to outline what decisions Dana and the Colemans need to make. To identify these decisions, you could say, *Lucas's transition to public school kindergarten certainly didn't go the way that Dana and the Colemans had hoped it would. What are the problems Dana is left to address at the end of the story? What decisions does she need to make?* Participants should, at a minimum, identify decisions that Dana needs to make related to Lucas's parents and the letter of complaint from Lynette Williams. After listing these problems on the board or flipchart, prompt the group to offer possible solutions. Questions related to Lucas's parents might include, *Should Dana encourage the Colemans to consider a compromise related to Lucas's placement? Should Dana support the Colemans' original desire to have Lucas placed in a regular kindergarten class? And, if so, how?* Be sure to encourage expression of alternative viewpoints and to consider carefully the possible outcomes of each option before a final decision is made. For example, if the group decides to support Lucas's parents in their original decision, you might ask, *In your own state/community, what rights would the Colemans have to appeal the committee's decision, and what would an appeal entail? What would be the probable outcome?* You might also want to ask, *Should Dana tell the Colemans about Lynette Williams's letter of complaint?*

Questions related to Lynette Williams's letter might include, *Glen Atwater has suggested that Dana should apologize to Lynette Williams about her behavior in the meeting. Should Dana apologize? What are the possible consequences if Dana decides not to apologize? How else could Dana handle the situation she is in with the administrators at Lochridge Children's Center and with Lynette Williams?*

In concluding this case discussion, you could ask participants a broad question about transition planning such as, *What lessons can we learn about transitions from Dana Tolliver's unfortunate experiences? Let's see if we can generate a quick list of dos and don'ts.* To begin generating this list, you may have to ask a few thought-provoking questions such as, *Can we ever adequately prepare families for their child's transition into public school?* With inservice audiences, you may want to take a more applied approach by asking participants what kindergarten transitions are like in their own state or community and how the process might be improved.

La Maestra

Topics

Cultural diversity, service coordination, hearing impairment, parent–professional partnerships, child abuse and neglect, professional boundaries, home-based services, family support services, infancy (from birth to age 3 years), low-income families, interagency coordination, siblings

Synopsis

Julio and Elena Martinez are illegal Mexican immigrants who came to the United States 4 years ago to take advantage of agricultural work opportunities they had heard about. The couple has five children, three girls and two boys, ranging in age from 19 months to 10 years. All three of the girls are profoundly deaf. Anne Lowrey has been providing home-based services to the family for approximately 1 year. Although Anne is responsible only for providing services to the Martinezes' youngest daughter, Isabella (19 months old), Anne feels as though she has sole responsibility for meeting the needs of the entire Martinez family, and their needs are many. Both parents are currently unemployed, and the family is living off the Supplemental Security Income checks (SSI) that Julio and Elena receive for their two youngest daughters. Protective services has removed the children from the home several times on the suspicion of abuse or neglect, and now Julio has been arrested and may soon be jailed or deported. Neither Julio nor Elena speak fluent English and they rely heavily on Anne to negotiate the various systems they must deal with, especially with regard to legal matters. They also count on Anne to teach their young daughters sign language. Although she is flattered by their trust in her, Anne is frustrated that Elena and Julio themselves don't use sign language with their daughters. Anne feels overwhelmed by the Martinez family's reliance on her and wonders why she seems to be the only one who is trying to hold this family together.

Major Issues

This case story addresses numerous issues that a service provider might encounter while providing home-based services, the most obvious of which is working with families from diverse cultural backgrounds. In this case story, cultural differences in family values are further complicated by language barriers and the fact that the parents are illegal immigrants. A second major issue this case story addresses is the service provider's ability to distinguish between providing enough support to a family and providing too much support, thereby prompting over-reliance or dependency. This is not any easy distinction to make. A third issue is what a service provider should do when he or she is confronted with parents who do not always appear to act within the best interest of their children. In this case, Julio and Elena Martinez have withdrawn one of their children from services and are not providing a signing environment for their daughters who are profoundly deaf. Finally, this story addresses the need for service coordination and interagency collaboration to create community support for families with multiple needs.

Teaching Notes

In light of the numerous problems confronting the service provider in this case story, it is probably best to begin by having the group outline all of the issues that need to be addressed. You might begin this discussion by saying, *Anne Lowrey certainly seems to have her hands full in working with the Martinez family. Let's begin by listing the challenges she has encountered. What problems is Anne trying to cope with?* Make a list of the identified problems on the board or flipchart, perhaps grouping related issues together as they are recognized. The group should, at a minimum, identify the problems and concerns that are listed below. Most groups will identify all of these issues and more. If they don't, you should direct their attention to the important issues that they have neglected to mention. The most prominent issues in this case include

- The Martinezes' failure to provide a signing environment for their daughters
- The Martinezes' decision to keep Carina home from preschool and Anne's ensuing assumption of responsibility for teaching Carina sign language
- Ensuring that the children's basic needs are met (supervision, health, safety, nutrition)
- The Martinezes' illegal immigrant status
- Cultural and language barriers
- Unemployment of parents (financial needs of family)
- Other professionals' and agencies' apparent lack of support for or understanding of the Martinez family(Carina's preschool teacher, Michael Santos)
- Julio's legal problems and the threat that he could be jailed or deported
- The family's dependence on Anne for their multiple needs (e.g., translation, legal matters, Carina) and Anne's feeling overwhelmed by her responsibilities

Next, you may want to review the list of issues with the group and ask participants whether they think Anne should, in fact, continue to assume responsibility for all of the Martinezes' problems. Particularly vocal groups may have already addressed this question in the process of generating the list, or you may have chosen to address this question yourself as participants identified the various problems. Questioning related to Anne's roles and responsibilities might also involve asking participants who they think *should be* responsible for the family's various needs if Anne isn't and whether they think these other agencies or professionals would actually do what needs to be done. Depending on the characteristics of your audience, you could also ask, *Would Anne be responsible for attending to these family needs if she were a home-based early interventionist (e.g., early childhood special educator)? The family's service coordinator? An allied health services provider (e.g., speech-language therapist, occupational therapist)? A consultant for the deaf and hard of hearing?* When working with inservice audiences, such questioning may lead to important discussions about the quality of service coordination in their own state or community.

If your teaching objectives also include family-centered practices (e.g., identifying family concerns, resources, and priorities), you may want to ask a few questions about the family at this point. You can open this topic by saying, *Elena and Julio certainly have a lot of problems. Do they have anything positive going for them at all? Can you identify any family strengths?* You could also ask, *Although we aren't provided with the parents' perspective in this story, what do you think Elena's and Julio's concerns or priorities might be for Isabella (the 19-month-old), for their other children, and for themselves?* Finally, if this has not been discussed previously, you might want to ask, *To what extent do you think Elena's and Julio's cultural values and practices have contributed to the problems described in this story?*

Next, you may want to spend a few minutes discussing Anne's relationship with the Martinezes and the actions that Anne has already taken. (*Note:* Some of these issues may have already been addressed during the identification of problems.) To introduce this topic, you might ask, *How do you think Anne Lowrey has done so far? Do you agree with the way she has handled the various situations she has encountered while working with the Martinez family? Would you have done anything differently?* You might follow this up with more specific questions, such as the following:

- *Why do you think Elena and Julio have come to trust Anne so much?*
- *Was it appropriate for Anne to have protected the Martinezes from Michael Santos (i.e., going to bat for them in order to have the children returned)? Could Anne be wrong in her conviction that Elena and Julio are "good parents" and that Julio would never intentionally hurt his children?*
- *Should Anne have been more insistent about getting Julio and Elena to use sign language with the girls? Does the Martinezes' failure to provide a signing environment for their daughters and their decision to keep Carina home from preschool constitute neglect?*
- *Would Anne be legally responsible in this state for reporting the illegal status of Elena and Julio or their relatives? If so, was Anne right not to have reported them?*
- *Should Anne have asked Elena and Julio where the money that they used to get Julio out of jail came from?*

These questions can result in some interesting and potentially lengthy discussions. For example, participants often express varying opinions about whether it was right for Anne to tell her daughter Collette about the Martinez family and to take Collette's old clothes and toys to the Martinez girls. Another issue that participants may raise and debate is the degree to which it is important to match a service provider's ethnic or cultural background with the background of the family receiving the services. This topic may also prompt a discussion about language barriers and the effects of using an interpreter versus employing a service provider who speaks the family's language. You will need to decide for yourself the depth in which you want the group to discuss these issues. You may also choose to discuss these topics in more detail at the conclusion of the case discussion rather than at this point.

To begin a discussion of the case's possible solutions, you could ask, *Of all the issues and problems we have discussed so far* (provide a brief summary), *which concern do you think Anne needs to deal with first? Where should she invest her energy? What issue is most important?* As participants offer their opinions, you may need to ask additional questions to prompt further exploration of the suggested solution. For example, depending on the group's responses, you might ask, *Is Anne really justified in attempting to keep this family together? Is this really what is best for the Martinez children?* Conversely, you might have cause to ask, *What will be the fate of this family if Julio is jailed or deported? Will any of these other issues really matter if he is?* If, however, you want the audience to solve a particular problem in the story, you could be more directive in beginning this phase of the discussion. For example, you might ask, *Let's look at the issue of* . . . [e.g., the parents' not signing to the children, the possibility of Julio's being deported]. *What options does Anne have for handling this problem?* Once you have identified an area for decision making, you can initiate the process of identifying alternative solutions, choosing among the various options, and planning a course of action for Anne to take. As always, remember to have the group consider the possible short- and long-term consequences of their decisions.

Toward the end of the case discussion, you may want to conduct a general discussion regarding one or more of the issues that this case story addresses (e.g., working with families whose cultural background, values, and language are different from your own; working with other agencies that are not "family-friendly"; working with parents who do not always act in the best interest of their children). If such a discussion is compatible with your teaching objectives, you might also want to ask participants about the eligibility status and resources available to families like the Martinezes who might live in the participants' own communities.

Heaven's Glory

Topics

Institutionalization, multiple and severe disabilities, family-centered practices, interprofessional conflicts, referrals, home-based services, infancy (from birth to age 3 years), family support services, father involvement

Synopsis

Sharon Keyes, a home-based early interventionist receives a referral from a local pediatrician. The new referral is 9-month-old Robert Turner, who has anencephaly; His brain scans show massive areas where cerebrospinal fluid has replaced brain matter. As Sharon begins her work with the Turner family, she wonders what hope there is to offer Robert's parents, who are obviously devastated by their new baby's irrevocable disabilities. To make matters worse, Ann Harrington, the child's pediatrician, has been talking to the family about institutionalizing the baby. After working with the Turner family for 3 months, Sharon believes that the issue of institutionalization has been dropped, but she discovers that she is mistaken when Mrs. Turner calls to tell Sharon that they have found an institutional placement for Robert. Sharon is shocked by the news and wonders what kind of parents the Turners are even to consider putting their baby in an institution, let alone to actually carry through with it. Sharon places most of the blame for what has happened on Ann Harrington; however, Sharon can't help thinking that she herself must somehow be at fault. But what has she done wrong? And is there anything she can still do to get the Turners to change their minds?

Major Issues

This case story challenges participants to consider a fairly extreme situation in early intervention. First, this story involves an infant who has little, if any, chance of making developmental progress, regardless of how intense any intervention efforts may be. What, then, is the role of the interventionist in this type of situation, and how do we measure or document our success? Second, the parents in this story have decided to institutionalize their infant son. Should this, then, be considered an instance in which early intervention has failed? These two issues raise important questions about the purpose and preferred outcomes of services for children and families and challenge participants to consider whether their personal values or program philosophies can be upheld when making decisions in such extreme situations. Another important issue that this story introduces is how to work with other professionals who may not share our philosophies; who may not cooperate with our policies and procedures; and who may even, at times, act in ways that are counterproductive to our own efforts in working with children and families.

Teaching Notes

In discussing this case story, you may want to start with the ending; that is, the Turners' decision to institutionalize Robert. By starting here, you will be able to assess where your audience stands with regard to this critical aspect of the story. You can initiate this discussion by saying, *At the end of the story, Sharon Keyes, the home-based service provider, is appalled that the parents are institutionalizing their baby and feels as though she has somehow failed in her job. What do you think about the Turners' decision to place Robert at Heaven's Glory? Is this a situation in which early intervention has failed? How would you feel if you were in Sharon's shoes?* In answering your questions, allow participants to freely express themselves, challenging them only to the extent needed to get them to provide reasons for their opinions and to ensure that alternative viewpoints are voiced. In an open discussion such as this, you can expect that participants will discuss various contributing factors in the situation, delve a little into issues of philosophy, and begin to offer solutions to the problem. This is fine; however, you may want to postpone any in-depth discussions of philosophy and potential solutions until later.

The next phase of the discussion should involve exploring the perspectives of the various characters in the story and the extent to which each character may have contributed to the problem(s). At a minimum, this should include a discussion of the home-based service provider (Sharon Keyes), the baby's parents (Emily and Steve Turner), and the pediatrician (Dr. Ann Harrington). You may be able to find a natural transition point during the opening discussion to initiate this phase of the discussion. If not, say something such as, *Let's stop here for a minute and back up in the story a little to see how this problem came about in the first place.*

Because Sharon Keyes is the main character (and it is from her perspective that the story is told), you should probably begin the discussion by asking, *What do you think about Sharon Keyes? Do you like her? Do you think she's done a good job working with the Turner family?* In all likelihood, participants will address most, if not all, of the important issues related to Sharon Keyes's behavior. If, however, some issues are overlooked, you may want to interject a few probing questions at appropriate points during the conversation. For example, you may want to ask about

- Sharon's interactions with the Turner family during her initial contact with them in Dr. Harrington's office
- Sharon's interactions with Emily Turner during the first home visit
- The appropriateness and sufficiency of respite care, feeding, and contingency awareness activities as interventions for the Turner family
- Whether Sharon should have broached the topic of institutionalization during home visits
- Whether Sharon should have tried harder to involve Steve Turner and, if so, how

You might also ask participants about the manner in which Sharon handled Ann Harrington as a way to guide the group into the next discussion topic—the pediatrician's contribution to the situation. Although the group does not need to spend a great deal of time discussing the pediatrician, it is sometimes helpful to have participants at least consider the possible motives behind Ann Harrington's behavior. You might open up this topic for discussion by saying, *Sharon seems to have some problems with the way Ann Harrington, the pediatrician, has handled the situation with the Turner family. What are some of these problems? Would you feel the same way as Sharon does about Ann Harrington? Would you do anything about it?* The discussion about Ann Harrington might include issues such as

1. The fact that Dr. Harrington waited 9 months to refer Robert to the early intervention program and that this referral was an autonomous decision on her part
2. The discussions about institutionalizing Robert that Dr. Harrington has obviously had with the Turners prior to making the referral to the early intervention program
3. Dr. Harrington's continued investigations into a residential placement for Robert without notifying Sharon

During the discussion of these issues, you may also want to ask, *Why might Ann Harrington have done these things? What possibly could have been going through her mind?*

Finally, you can ask the group to consider the Turners' perspectives. You might begin by saying, *When Emily announces that they have found a residential placement for Robert, Sharon is shocked. She asks herself what kind of a mother would do such a thing and wonders if Steve has forced Emily into this decision or if, perhaps, she has just been wrong about Emily all along. Why might the Turners have continued to pursue institutionalization?* You can extend the discussion by asking questions such as, *What might contribute to a family's decision to place such a young child in an institution? What are the costs to a family (emotional, physical, financial) in caring for a child such as Robert at home? Is institutionalization really such an awful decision for a child like Robert? Would institutionalization even be an option for families living in your state or community? If not, what other options are available?*

After discussing the perspectives of the various characters in this story, direct the discussion toward decision making by asking, *What do you think Sharon should do next?* The most important decision that needs to be made is with regard to Robert's impending placement at Heaven's Glory. In making this decision, you could ask the participants, *Should Sharon try to get the Turners to reconsider their decision? Or should Sharon just consider Robert's impending placement at Heaven's Glory a done deal?* If participants think that Sharon should try to get the Turners to reconsider their decision, ask them to describe how she should go about doing this, perhaps even identifying the exact words she should use. Be certain that participants also consider how the Turners might react to attempts aimed at getting them to change their minds (e.g., *How might Sharon's attempts to get the Turners to change their minds make them feel?*). You might further ask, *Suppose the Turners follow through with their plan to institutionalize Robert. Should Sharon honor their request that she accompany them when they take Robert to Heaven's Glory?* Then you could ask, *Do you think Sharon should have any further contact with Robert or his family after his placement? If so, what should be the nature of such contact?* Finally, participants could revisit issues related to the pediatrician during this phase of the discussion. For example, participants' decisions may involve having Sharon contact the pediatrician in order to get the Turners to reconsider their decision.

The decisions that participants reach regarding what Sharon should do about Robert's institutionalization are not as important as the reasons behind their decisions. This story lends itself well to explorations of personal beliefs and how such beliefs can influence our perspectives on families and the decisions that we make. The issues in this case challenge some important philosophical principles in early intervention, perhaps even pitting one philosophy against another (e.g., inclusion and quality of life versus family-centered practices). Uncovering these issues may require you to repeatedly prompt participants to provide rationales for their decisions. This may be achieved by asking, *Why do you think that?* or by reflecting participants' feelings (e.g., *It sounds as though you feel strongly about this issue. Why?*) When appropriate, you might also challenge participants' decisions by asking them to consider alternative perspectives. For example, you might ask, *Would that be the best thing for Emily Turner? For Steve Turner? For Robert? For Robert's siblings Joey and Sarah?* At some point, you could also ask, *Would you feel the same way if the Turners were placing Robert in foster care?*

In concluding the discussion of this case story, you could expand on any of the story's major issues. What you choose to focus on, however, should reflect both your primary teaching objectives and the issues that seemed particularly important or challenging to the group.

Supplemental Materials

Money Matters

Purpose

The decisions that Judy and Randy Seagroves make are likely to depend on the types of resources that are available to them within their community. One of the roles of an early interventionist is to provide information about these resources. The purpose of this activity is to explore the various types of resources that are available within your *own* community that may be useful to the Seagroves family in developing strategies to address their concerns and priorities.

Format

For this activity, you will be assigned to a "team" that will meet together to 1) discuss the various types of resources that may be useful to the Seagroves family, 2) share any information that your team members already possess about resources and services within the community, and 3) decide what additional resources the Seagroves family might find useful and determine what additional information is needed about resources with which your team members are already familiar.

Your team should assign responsibilities to each individual member for collecting the necessary information within the next week or two.

Information Gathering and Reporting

You may make telephone calls or visits to agencies within the community to gather information. You may also contact secondary resources (e.g., consumers of services, other agencies in the community). The types of information that you investigate may include eligibility requirements, the cost of services, the types of services rendered, the current availability of the services, the duration of services, and consumer satisfaction with the services. Most important, you should determine whether the services rendered by the various agencies are likely to be useful to the Seagroves family. Will the services address the Seagroveses' specific needs and concerns? Are the services practical for this family's lifestyle?

In addition to providing information about each potential resource, you should keep notes about how you gathered your information. The notes should include your strategies for finding information, whom you contacted, the amount of time that it took to gather the information, and your perception of how friendly and helpful each contact was.

Your team will be responsible for completing a "Community Resource Fact Sheet" for each potential resource that it identifies. In addition to these fact sheets, your team may also gather brochures, parent booklets, application forms, or other information that is available from each community resource. Once your team has identified the available resources, transfer your findings to the Team Summary Worksheet located on page 73.

COMMUNITY RESOURCE FACT SHEET

Your name: _____

Team members: _____

1. Name of program or agency:

   _____

2. Address or location:

   _____

3. Type of resource:

   _____

4. Contact person and job position:

   _____

5. How did you gather your information about this resource (e.g., telephone call, visit, secondary resource, previous experience)?

   _____

6. Approximately how much of your time was involved in gathering information?

   _____

7. How satisfied were you with the level, type, and clarity of information that you were able to gather?

   _____

   _____

8. Briefly describe the type of service or assistance provided by this resource:

   _____

   _____

   _____

   _____

   _____

9. What qualifications or eligibility criteria does this resource require?

   _____

   _____

   _____

   _____

   _____

(continued)

Instructor's Guide for Lives in Progress, McWilliam, © 2000 Paul H. Brookes Publishing Co.

10. What is the availability of this service and what level of assistance can this service provide (e.g., waiting lists, time lag between request and when services begin, duration of services, frequency of services, limitations of services)?

_____

_____

_____

_____

_____

11. What are the costs of this service?

_____

_____

_____

_____

12. How much time and effort will be required to procure these services (e.g., interviews, completing application forms)?

_____

_____

_____

_____

_____

13. How might this resource be useful to the Seagroves family in addressing their priorities and concerns?

_____

_____

_____

_____

14. Briefly describe any reservations that you might have about the usefulness or appropriateness of this resource for the Seagroves family:

_____

_____

_____

_____

_____

The Seagroves Family Team Summary	
Family Concern or Priority	Potential Resource(s)
1.	
2.	
3.	
4.	
5.	
6.	

At the Close of the Day

Although students or practitioners may come to understand and believe in family-centered principles, they may still have difficulty with applying these principles to their direct interactions with families. In teaching with the case method, role plays and team simulations provide opportunities for students to practice their communication skills within the context of a relatively nonthreatening environment. Described below are two instructional activities that I have developed for "At the Close of the Day." I have designed both of these activities for use after the group discussion of "Recipe for Rachel."

Activity #1: Understanding Family Concerns, Priorities, and Resources (Role Play)

Following a full discussion of "Recipe for Rachel," participants should be divided into pairs. One member of each pair will assume the role of Gwen Roland. The other member of the pair will take on the role of Sandy Stevens and should be given a copy of the story, "At the Close of the Day." After pairs and roles have been identified, divide the participants into two groups according to the role that they have been given (Gwen or Sandy). Those participants who are playing the role of Sandy should leave the classroom for about 20 minutes. They should use this time to read "At the Close of the Day" and prepare themselves for a subsequent conversation with their partners who will be playing the role of Gwen Roland. It might also be useful to provide additional information about Prader-Willi syndrome to participants who are playing the role of Sandy Stevens. This information could consist of brochures from the National Prader-Willi Association, journal articles, summaries of research findings, newsletter clippings, or magazine articles. Excellent information is also available through the Internet. For example, try http://www.pwsausa.org.

While those playing Sandy Stevens are reading and preparing for the role play, you should lead a discussion with the group of participants who will play Gwen Roland. The group should quickly review the issues that Gwen faces in working with Rachel Stevens and her family and what they already know or assume to be Sandy's concerns, priorities, and resources. (*Note:* If this activity follows shortly after a group discussion of "Recipe for Rachel," much of this information will already have been identified.) The primary purpose of this discussion is to identify the issues that Gwen Roland should address in her upcoming conversation with Sandy Stevens in order to better understand the Stevens family's perspective (i.e., concerns, priorities, and resources). You should make a list of the issues that are generated by the participants as the discussion proceeds.

These activities are intended to be used with "Recipe for Rachel," Chapter 15 of the accompanying text.

Next, ask all of the participants who are playing the role of Gwen Roland to join their partners who are playing the role of Sandy Stevens and find a quiet place where they can talk. Allow the pairs to converse for at least 20–30 minutes. While the participants are talking, walk around from pair to pair and listen discreetly to see how the participants are doing and to gauge when to end this phase of the activity. However, intervene in the conversation only if a pair is at a complete standstill. When appropriate, and close to the pre-allotted time limit, ask all of the participants to reconvene in the classroom.

Content Debriefing   A full group discussion should take place at this point. This discussion will probably require 45 minutes to an hour. You should address two major topics during the discussion: First, the content of information obtained from Sandy Stevens, and second, the communication skills used by those playing Gwen Roland. You can begin the discussion by asking those who played the role of Gwen Roland what additional information they learned through their conversations with Sandy Stevens. Were their previous assumptions about the Stevens family's concerns, priorities, and resources accurate? Did Sandy Stevens convey any new or surprising information to the participants who were playing the part of Gwen? How might the participants' revised views of the Stevens family's priorities affect intervention strategies? Although those participants who played the part of Gwen Roland are first asked to respond to your questions, participants who played the role of Sandy may gradually be permitted to join in the conversation.

Process Debriefing   Following a discussion of the content of the pairs' conversations, those participants who played the role of Sandy Stevens should be asked to comment about the types and quality of communication skills that their partners used. It is best to begin with the positive. This can be accomplished by posing a question such as, *What did the person playing Gwen say or do that made you, in the role of a parent, feel comfortable to share information and feelings about yourself and your family?* The group will typically contribute comments about body language, tone of voice, listening, and so forth. If participants make vague comments, such as "I felt respected" or, "She seemed to understand what I was feeling," you should pose follow-up questions about what the person playing Gwen actually said or did to make the participant feel that way.

This discussion allows the group to identify specific and concrete communication strategies that are effective in working with families. You should make a list of the positive communication skills on the board or flipchart as the participants identify them. Negative feelings about what Gwen said or did will also usually emerge throughout the course of this discussion. If not, you may wish to introduce this topic of discussion. In talking about ineffective communication skills, however, you should encourage participants to identify positive and effective alternatives that professionals could use in their work with families.

This role-play activity can be modified by having more than one person play the role of Gwen Roland per each person playing the role of Sandy. If you decide to use this method, those playing Gwen should share responsibility for talking with the person playing Sandy, taking turns as they see fit. It is recommended, however, that no more than two or three people play the role of Gwen with each Sandy.

Activity #2: Developing Intervention Plans with Families

This activity may be done by itself; in conjunction with "Activity #1: Understanding Family Concerns, Priorities, and Resources" (Role Play) (see the previous activity); or following the completion of Activity #1. The purpose of this activity is to provide participants with an opportunity to practice applying a family-centered approach in the development of a written individualized family service plan (IFSP) or individualized education program (IEP). More specifically, this activity focuses on active parent participation in the IFSP/IEP conference and on translating family concerns, resources, and priorities into written goals and objectives. Similar to Activity #1, this activity emphasizes practice in communicating with families.

Participants should be divided into groups. At a minimum, each role-play group will consist of one person playing the role of Sandy Stevens and one person playing the role of Gwen Roland. Each group may, however, be expanded to include two to four participants playing the role of a professional and one participant assuming the role of Sandy Stevens (team simulation). Groups larger than this may not afford each member playing the role of a professional sufficient opportunity to practice his or her communication skills. You may or may not wish to identify the disciplines to which the "professionals" within each small group belong. This will depend on your teaching objectives. (*Note:* All participants should have read "Recipe for Rachel" prior to this activity, and those playing the role of Sandy Stevens should also have read "At the Close of the Day.")

Participants should be instructed that the purpose of this role-play or team simulation is to arrive at a written list of outcomes or goals for Rachel's IFSP or IEP. Your teaching objectives and the amount of time that is available for this activity will determine the level of detail that each IFSP or IEP should entail. At a minimum, each group should identify and write down three to five goals for the intervention plan. If more time is available, you may increase the required number of goals and/or ask each group to develop objectives, intervention strategies, and evaluation criteria for each goal. This activity assumes that participants have had prior information and/or discussions regarding recommended practices in the development and writing of family-centered intervention plans.

Following the completion of the role play or team simulation, all participants should reconvene to compare and discuss their results. Each pair or team should be asked to present the goals that they have developed. You should make a written list of the goals on a board or flipchart in the front of the room. If your group includes a large number of participants, you can save time by asking each team or pair to present only their top-priority goal(s). The participants should also discuss the process that they used to identify goals for the IFSP/IEP. Those participants who played the role of Sandy Stevens may be able to provide interesting insight into this aspect of the activity. You may use the questions on the next page ("The IFSP/IEP Conference: Questions for Discussion") to facilitate this discussion. Or, as an alternative, you may conclude this discussion by asking participants to develop their own checklist or guidelines for professionals to use while conducting IFSP/IEP conferences and writing intervention plans.

The IFSP/IEP Conference: Questions for Discussion

1. During the conference, did the parent talk as much as the professionals?

2. Was the parent asked about her thoughts, feelings, and ideas regarding possible outcomes and strategies? Was the parent asked these questions before suggestions were offered by professionals?

3. Did conversations about outcomes and strategies include acknowledging the child's strengths?

4. Did conversations about outcomes and strategies address family strengths (i.e., skills, knowledge, resources)?

5. Was the parent the ultimate decision maker?

6. Do the outcomes and strategies address child development/skills in environments other than the classroom (e.g., home, public places)?

7. Are outcomes written using words that are familiar to the family (i.e., easily understood and relevant to the family)?

8. Were the next steps in the planning and intervention process explained and discussed?

9. Was the parent offered a copy of the written plan?

10. Who has the primary responsibility for carrying out the plan? Are strategies identified for multiple environments?

11. Are outcomes likely to be achieved within a relatively short period of time? In other words, will progress be readily evident?

At the Close of the Day

P.J. McWilliam and Kathryn Matthews

Sandy dismissed the twins, Kimberly and Matthew, from the kitchen to watch their favorite Friday night television program. Dennis was already in the living room with Jessica and Rachel, but he obviously wasn't paying much attention to what the girls were doing. Even from the kitchen Sandy could hear their squabbling, and Dennis wasn't doing anything to stop it. She wished he would take his responsibility for the children more seriously; but then, Dennis had problems of his own. He was in pain most of the time or sleepy from the medicine he used to relieve the pain. There were times when Sandy longed for the Dennis she had known before the accident and wondered what life would be like now if the accident had never happened.

Standing at the kitchen sink, washing the last of the pots and pans from dinner, Sandy looked out the window at the backyard. Beyond the rusty swing set and the dried remains of her summer vegetable garden, a winter sun was setting behind the row of pine trees that divided their land from the land that belonged to the neighboring farmer. Even in December, there was a peacefulness about this place that comforted her. Yes, she was glad they had made the move out to the country. It didn't matter that the house was small and needed a lot of work that they couldn't afford. It would still be a good place for Rachel to live—a safe oasis for her when the world was unkind. That was one of the main reasons for moving: to provide Rachel with a home where she could escape the gawking and taunting of other children that seemed inevitable as she grew older.

As Sandy watched the now crimson-orange sun dip below the level of the tree tops, she began thinking about the party at Rachel's school earlier in the day. All together, the event had been enjoyable; however, a few things had happened that had upset her, and these incidents nagged at the back of her mind. First, there was the reaction of the other parents when Rachel told Santa Claus that all she wanted for Christmas was juice and cookies. They all thought it was so cute and sweet, but Sandy didn't. It horrified her. Why couldn't Rachel have said she wanted a doll carriage or a stuffed animal or *anything* other than food? At age 3, Rachel was already showing signs of obsessing over food. It also bothered Sandy that Gwen Roland, Rachel's teacher, had been among those who had smiled about Rachel's request to Santa. Sandy had spent hours talking with Gwen about Prader-Willi syndrome. She had thought Gwen understood, but obviously she didn't—or at least not completely.

Then there was the incident over the cupcakes. The collective look of disapproval from the other parents and the teachers when Sandy punished Rachel for begging was almost overwhelming. From the looks on their faces, she felt as though horns had suddenly sprouted out of the top of her head. Of course no one had said a word, but the message was nonetheless perfectly clear. They all thought she was being unreasonably strict with Rachel. Why must she always be the bad guy? She had thought she would be used to it by now, but she wasn't. It still hurt deeply to have others think she was a bad mother.

The same thing happened at church. Every social function seemed to involve food, and most of it was high-calorie food that Rachel couldn't have. Sandy usually allowed Rachel to have some vegetables and a roll, but she didn't let her have the cakes and other sweets that were always laid out so temptingly on the tables. Rachel would ask imploringly for the desserts, and sometimes she would pitch an outright fit when she didn't get them. Sandy dealt with Rachel's begging and tantrums by making her stand in a corner for 5 minutes, but well-meaning friends and church members frequently interfered with Sandy's discipline. When they saw Rachel getting into trouble they would say, "Rachel, come over here with me for a little while," and pull her out of the situation. On more than one occasion, Sandy had been admonished with comments such as, "Rachel is too young to understand," and "You can't just keep saying 'no' to her all the time."

With only a faint orange afterglow remaining in the western sky, Sandy flipped the switch above the kitchen counter. The stark white light of the fluorescent fixture flickered on, and she began vigorously scrubbing the last pot. The anger and frustration that had welled up inside her fueled the motion of the sponge. Round and round the inside of the pot she scrubbed, pushing harder and harder against the aluminum walls. Tears of sadness welled up in her eyes, but she would not let them fall; there had been too much of that already. She had to be strong for Rachel's sake. For no matter what anyone else thought of her, Sandy knew she was doing the right thing.

Sandy rinsed the pot, placed it on the drainboard, and whisked her hands along the sides of her jeans to dry them. She heard Dennis tell Kimberly to take Rachel upstairs and get her ready for bed. Then she listened to Rachel as she tried to plead her way out of the situation. Rather than go into the living room to intercede as she usually would, Sandy poured herself a glass of water from the sink and slowly sipped it as she listened to Rachel play on the sympathies of Dennis and Kimberly.

Sandy had always considered it a blessing that Rachel's cognitive abilities and speech were not significantly delayed. Many children with Prader-Willi syndrome were not as fortunate. Sandy had thought that Rachel's abilities would make a big difference in handling the challenges that lay ahead of them. She had thought she would be able to talk to Rachel—to reason with her—and that, by doing so, Rachel could be made to understand her condition and why she needed to control her diet. But Sandy thought differently now. Although she was still pleased with Rachel's progress, she worried now that Rachel's relatively advanced speech might actually help her to get around the restrictions of her diet. After all, she was only 3 years old, and she was already an expert manipulator.

As Sandy sipped her water, she looked around the kitchen. Rachel's lunchbox was still sitting beside the back door where Sandy had put it when she and Rachel had arrived home from preschool. Sandy sat her glass on the table and retrieved the lunchbox. There's always one more thing after the dishwater is emptied, she thought. Oh well, it's Friday. It can wait until tomorrow. She opened the lunchbox and placed the plastic containers beside the sink. Making Rachel's lunch was one thing that Sandy didn't particularly like to do. It wasn't that it was difficult, it was just that it was one of the last chores of the evening, and Sandy was usually tired.

At the beginning of the year, Rachel's lunch had been the school's responsibility. Sandy had spent a good deal of time talking with the cafeteria staff about Rachel's diet, but they never got it right. Gwen had tried intervening with the cafeteria staff, but Sandy eventually just gave up and started packing Rachel's lunch. It was too important not to get it right. Gwen had also worked with Sandy to develop a menu of snack foods for the other parents to use as a guide when it was their turn to provide the snack for the classroom. Gwen had been so positive that the menu would work that Sandy had also developed high hopes. But within a few months there were problems. The parents started sending in snacks that Rachel was not supposed to have, and reminders from

Gwen about the importance of sticking to the snack list were only temporarily effective. Birthday parties and other special events that took place in the classroom also tempted Rachel with food that she wasn't allowed to have. Although Sandy had hoped it could be different, she eventually concluded that she couldn't postpone the inevitable. Rachel would have to learn at an early age that she was different from other children and that there were foods she just couldn't have.

Sandy had also decided against Dr. Laettner's suggestion that Rachel be allowed to have raw vegetables and fruits whenever she wanted them. What good would it do Rachel to think she could eat any time she wanted to? Rachel had to learn that there were times to eat and times not to eat. Consequently, Rachel was only allowed to eat at mealtimes and during pre-set snack times. Carrot sticks were one of Rachel's favorite snacks. Sandy always told her that they made her hair the prettiest color of red this side of heaven.

Rachel's high-fiber, low-sugar, low-fat, low-sodium diet affected everyone in the household. Rachel's diet required Sandy to buy higher grades of meat in order to cut down on fat and fresh vegetables rather than sodium-laden canned vegetables. Though these extra expenses strained the family's budget, it was worth it. For Rachel, it was a matter of life and death. Sandy had also learned to cook differently. For example, she substituted applesauce for shortening while making biscuits and cakes, and cooking oil was completely eliminated from all food preparations. Dennis and the other children didn't always appreciate the changes in the family's meals, but Sandy was firm about not giving in to their complaining. This was a family, and everyone had to make some sacrifices.

One of the biggest sacrifices for the other three children was the limitations that Sandy imposed on their snacking. No eating was allowed outside mealtimes when Rachel was around. If they wanted cookies, pretzels, or fruit, they had to wait until Rachel was taking her nap or they had to find a place to eat outside where Rachel couldn't see them. This sacrifice was probably hardest on Matthew who, at age 13, was hungry all the time. Even in the cold and rain of December, he made frequent trips out the back door with his pockets full of food. But Rachel was beginning to outsmart him. Dennis had had to install locks on the food cabinets and the trash can to keep Rachel out of them but she had developed a keen ear for the sound of the cabinets being unlocked and she raced toward the kitchen whenever she heard this distinctive noise. More than once, Matthew's clandestine snacking had been thwarted by Rachel's unexpected arrival in the kitchen.

No matter how hard it was, it was all worth it. Sandy and Dennis were lucky to have learned that Rachel had Prader-Willi syndrome as early as they did. Most families didn't find out until their children were at least 5 or 6 years old and already obese. Some families didn't find out until much later than that. Sandy didn't plan on wasting the head start that they had been given through Rachel's early diagnosis. Sandy had read everything about Prader-Willi syndrome that she could get her hands on. Much of the information she had acquired was given to her by Lynne Casto, the director of the group home in Quail Crossroads. Lynne had also put her in touch with the National Prader-Willi Association, and the people there had sent Sandy a lot of information and a copy of *The Gathered View,* a newsletter in which parents of children with Prader-Willi syndrome told their stories. Although Sandy couldn't afford to join the national association and subscribe to the newsletter, she planned on doing so next year if she and Dennis had the money. Meanwhile, Sandy read the materials she had over and over again.

The things that Sandy had read about Prader-Willi syndrome scared her to death; however, when the disapproval of others caused her to question what she was doing, she read them again to strengthen her resolve. Sandy knew that although children with Prader-Willi syndrome typically started out their lives as Rachel had, with difficulty with eating and poor weight gain, by the time they were 2 or 3 years old the first signs of insatiable hunger began. At age 5 or 6, their hunger drives became even stronger, though the real problems didn't begin until the early onset of puberty at age 10 or 11. Sandy still didn't understand how the children could begin puberty early but never reach full sexual maturity, but she supposed she would find out soon enough. If uncontrolled, the incredible amount of weight that children with Prader-Willi syndrome gained could result in respiratory problems, diabetes, and heart problems, which, in turn, could lead to an early death. Included among the letters that Sandy had read in *The Gathered View* were two tributes that parents had written about their children who had died as young adults. Sandy knew that Rachel's asthma made her even more susceptible to respiratory difficulties, and this made Sandy even more determined to control Rachel's weight.

Lynne Casto had told Sandy that people with Prader-Willi syndrome also tend to have brittle bones and a high pain tolerance. In combination, these two conditions could result in undetected fractures. Sandy had already noticed Rachel's high pain tolerance. Rachel watched the nurses draw her blood without a wince, rarely cried when she fell, and always seemed to have bruises from falls that Sandy had been unaware of having ever happened. Given Rachel's poor balance, Sandy was concerned that she might be hurt seriously one day just from doing the things that other children her age were doing: climbing on the furniture, running out in the yard, or swinging on a swing. The fact that Rachel was already overweight only added to her awkwardness and, therefore, made her more prone to having accidents. Sandy knew that Rachel needed more than just dieting to control her weight. She also needed physical activity to burn off calories. Without adult prodding, however, Rachel usually preferred quiet play, sometimes to the point of appearing lethargic.

Aside from the issues of health and safety, Sandy was shocked to learn about the effects of obesity on intelligence. Lynne Casto had shown her an article from a medical journal in which researchers had found that there was a direct relationship between weight and IQ score. In the study, 27 children with Prader-Willi syndrome between the ages of 2 and 17 years were given an intelligence test. Those children whose weight had been well controlled from the time they were young had a significantly higher IQ score (mean IQ score = 80.25) than those children who were obese and had never undergone treatment (mean IQ score = 59.90) and those children who had been obese but had later lost a significant amount of weight (mean IQ score = 57.33). Rachel could be like the children in the first group. She just had to be.

From all that Sandy had learned about Prader-Willi syndrome, what scared her most were the emotional and behavioral difficulties associated with the disorder. These were the demons of the future. On good days, Sandy had hopes that Rachel's early diagnosis and the family's concerted efforts to do what was necessary for Rachel would pave the way for the future. But there were other times when she wondered whether she would be prepared for the battles that lay ahead. As children with Prader-Willi syndrome grew older, many of them developed socialization and behavior problems. Some even became violent and, although their violence was typically related to food, it could lead to their eventual institutionalization.

Children with Prader-Willi syndrome were known to do anything for food. They would trade their own possessions for food out of their classmates' lunchboxes, and they would even steal items from their classmates to trade for food or to sell in order to get money to buy food. There was no limit. The chances were that Sandy and Dennis, like other families of children with Prader-Willi syndrome before them, would have to go from door to door to notify neighbors about Rachel's potential for stealing food and money. They would also have to notify the police authorities in their community. Although Dennis supported Sandy's efforts to control Rachel's weight, he would not engage in conversations about the future. Neither would anyone else. Whenever Sandy tried to talk about the future, she was told not to worry and that things would probably be different for Rachel. But Sandy was worried, and she believed that she faced these demons alone.

Dennis's cane rapped on the door frame, startling Sandy. "Hey, what are you doing in here?" he asked.

"Just thinking," replied Sandy. She glanced quickly at the clock on the stove. She had been lost in her thoughts and hadn't realized how late it was getting.

"Well, you know how I feel about that," said Dennis. "You shouldn't think so much. It's dangerous."

Dennis was right, but Sandy couldn't help herself. She looked at him standing in the doorway of the kitchen, leaning forward with both hands resting on the top of his cane. Maybe he doesn't take the responsibility he should for the children, she thought, but he does take responsibility for me. Despite his own problems, Dennis had found the energy to worry about Sandy and to take care of her during those first few months after Rachel was born. Those months had been traumatic for Sandy. She had worried constantly about how difficult it was to feed Rachel, and the baby's frequent hospitalizations had exhausted Sandy both physically and emotionally. Dennis's strength and support had seen her through those difficult times. She knew she could always count on him when she needed him most.

"Rachel's in bed and wants you to tuck her in," said Dennis. He turned around and walked back into the living room.

Sandy went into the bedroom that all three girls shared and sat on the bottom bunk to tuck in Rachel. They said prayers together, and Sandy rubbed Rachel's back until she was almost asleep. Tucking the covers around the child's shoulders, Sandy noticed that the sore on Rachel's arm was now raw and angry looking. Lynne had told Sandy that children with Prader-Willi syndrome will often scratch and pick at their wounds, and, because of this constant irritation, it could take up to a year or more for a wound to heal completely. Rachel had only just begun this type of behavior over the past few months, but it seemed to get worse with each passing week. Sandy wasn't sure what she should do about it, but she would have to come up with something soon. Sandy carefully wrapped the corner of the sheet around Rachel's arm, hoping that it might prevent her from scratching it. Then she leaned forward and kissed Rachel's forehead.

"Nite-nite, Mommy," said Rachel in a sleepy voice.

"Goodnight, sweetheart," said Sandy. She looked at the child's face, dimly lit by the yellow glow of the nightlight on the dresser. "Dear Lord, give me strength to do what I must for this precious child that you have entrusted to my care," she said softly. Then she stood up to leave.

"Mommy?" said a voice from the upper bunk.

"Yes?" Sandy hadn't realized that 8-year-old Jessica was already in bed, too.

"Will you tuck me in?" asked Jessica sheepishly.

"That's a little hard to do up on that top bunk, but lean down here and I'll give you a goodnight kiss. How about that?"

Jessica leaned over the side of the bed, kissed her mother goodnight, and smiled before lying back down.

The forgotten child, thought Sandy, as she turned and walked out of the bedroom. Jessica had been ignored and bounced around from relative to relative after Dennis's accident and throughout the following 2 years as he underwent one surgery after another. Jessica was just a toddler when that had happened. Then she was ignored again after Rachel was born. Sometimes Sandy felt as though Kimberly had spent more time with Jessica than she had during the first 2 years after Rachel was born.

What would she do without Kimberly? Dennis may have been who she counted on for emotional support, but it was Kimberly who she counted on to give her a helping hand around the house. She often asked Kimberly to sweep the floor, wash the dishes, or fold the laundry. And it was Kimberly who gave Rachel a bath or entertained the younger girls when Sandy was busy. Sometimes Sandy got angry at Kimberly for spoiling Rachel and giving in to her begging, but her anger was fleeting. She knew that Kimberly loved Rachel with all her heart. Although Kimberly was 13 years old, she was still young. She couldn't be expected to comprehend the fears that Sandy had about Rachel's future.

Sandy returned to the living room, where Dennis and the twins were engrossed in a movie on the television. Kimberly and Matthew took turns reaching into a bag of chips that sat between them on the couch. Sandy settled into a chair and reached into her sewing basket for Dennis's dress shirt that needed a button replaced. As she pulled a length of thread from the spool, she glanced again at the twins. She remembered the delightful moments she had shared with them when they were toddlers, but they were made to grow up so fast. Would they also be asked to carry the torch when she and Dennis could no longer care for Rachel? That responsibility would probably fall on Kimberly, thought Sandy. Kimberly was the more responsible of the two, and she already showed a strong protective instinct where Rachel was concerned.

Contemplating the future, a sudden and terrifying thought flashed through Sandy's mind: Kimberly wouldn't have to take responsibility for Rachel if Rachel died at an early age. The thought of one of her children dying before she did sent a cold shudder through her entire body. This was the future that Sandy couldn't think about. She snapped a length of thread from the spool, took a deep breath, and quickly refocused her mind on sewing.

What Color Is Forever?

Parents' reactions to the initial diagnosis of their child's disability and the impact that the disability has on the family are frequently described in textbooks and journal articles. The purpose of this story and the suggested teaching activities is to provide students or trainees with a parent's perspective on these topics. By viewing the Eason family's situation through Kaye Eason's eyes, students and trainees should come to a better understanding of the experiences, thoughts, fears, worries, and hopes that contribute to what professionals so often simply label "denial." This is also an excellent story for understanding the impacts of a child's disability on his or her family and for comprehending the importance of addressing family concerns and priorities other than those directly related to the health and development of the child with disabilities.

Described below are two instructional activities that I have developed for "What Color Is Forever?" Both of these activities are designed to be used following a group discussion of "An Uncertain Future." Both activities emphasize the importance of understanding a family's concerns, resources, and priorities prior to offering specific services or developing intervention plans. You should choose only one of these two activities to use with your group of trainees. The skill level of participants, the amount of time available, and your teaching objectives will determine which activity to use with your particular group. The major difference between the two activities is that Activity #2 (role play) offers the added benefit of having trainees practice and discuss communication skills.

Activity #1: Exploring Parent Perspectives

Prior to using "What Color Is Forever?," you should ask the participants to generate a list of the goals of service provision (i.e., what participants think are priorities for Shannon and her family and what types of services might be useful in addressing each priority). Participants should also discuss their perceptions of the Eason family. Both of these issues were probably covered during the group discussion of "An Uncertain Future." Even so, you will want to spend a few minutes recapping these aspects of the discussion prior to starting this new activity. Questions for identifying possible goals and priorities could include: *Based on the available information, what do you think should be the focus of intervention? What needs to be accomplished, and how might this be done?* To prompt the group to offer their perceptions of the Eason family, you could ask, *What do we know about Kaye Eason? How do you think Kaye Eason might be feeling about her daughter Shannon?* and, *What do you think it would feel like to be in Kaye Eason's shoes? What thoughts and concerns might she be experiencing?*

These activities are intended to be used with "An Uncertain Future," Chapter 17 of the accompanying text.

To prepare for this activity, you should ask each participant to read a copy of "What Color Is Forever?," briefly explaining that this is the perception of Shannon's mother, Kaye Eason. Instruct participants to take note of the Eason family's concerns, priorities, and resources as the participants read along. After the participants have read the story, you should initiate a group discussion. You can begin by asking a simple question, such as, *What do you know about Kaye Eason that you didn't know before?* or, *Were your initial impressions or assumptions about Kaye correct?* Facilitating only when necessary, allow the group to continue talking about Kaye's experiences, concerns, hopes, and priorities. Make a list of the identified family issues and concerns on the board or flipchart.

Next, ask the group to look at the list of issues and concerns that they have identified, and ask them to compare this list to the previously generated list of intervention goals. For example, you could ask, *How would our previous list of goals and services change based on what we now know about Kaye Eason and her family?* This discussion can be rather unstructured, or you can ask the group to develop a new list of child and family priorities along with intervention or service strategies to address each priority. Typically, during this aspect of the discussion, there will be an increased awareness of family-level goals. As the group identifies family goals, you might want to ask them who would be responsible for meeting each of these goals (e.g., *Are all early interventionists expected to deal with this type of family issue? Would you feel confident in this area?*). You may also have to remind the group to consider informal sources of support to address some family-level goals.

In concluding this activity, you might ask some of the following types of questions:

- *How important is it for interventionists to have the type of information that you have just read about in this story (i.e., parents' perspective)?*
- *What are the possible consequences of not knowing the parent's perspective?*
- *How can programs and individual service providers obtain such information from families? Who should obtain the information and how? How can we guard against intrusiveness?*
- *Would all families be willing to disclose the type of personal information that the family in this situation disclosed? If not, under what circumstances are parents most likely to be open about their feelings and priorities?*

Activity #2: Understanding Family Concerns, Priorities, and Resources (Role Play)

As stated previously, role-playing this situation rather than just reading the story to obtain Kaye Eason's perspective provides the participants with an opportunity to practice and discuss communication skills. Role playing does, however, require additional time, because the group will be discussing both *content* and *process* issues. The procedures for conducting this role play are identical to those described in the suggested teaching activities for "At the Close of the Day" (See "Activity #1: Understanding Family Concerns, Priorities, and Resources (Role Play)," pp. 74–75). Following the role play, the group may discuss *content* issues in a manner similar to that described for "Activity #1: Exploring Parent Perspectives." The discussion of *process* issues (i.e., communication skills) should follow the guidelines included in Activity #1 for "At the Close of the Day."

What Color Is Forever?

P.J. McWilliam

Kaye Eason leaned against the kitchen counter and thought about the woman from the early intervention program who would be coming out to the house today to see Shannon. Kaye wasn't certain what Beth Mason would actually be doing with Shannon, but it probably wouldn't hurt to hear what she had to say. Then again, Kaye wasn't so sure how much more she could take. She was still reeling from the news that the family had received from Dr. Sharpe a little over a month ago. Kaye's whole world seemed to have changed after that, and yet, nothing had really changed at all.

The Easons had first found out about Shannon's eye problems when she was 8 weeks old. Shannon had finally weighed 2 pounds and had been taken off the hospital's critical list. In celebration, Kaye and Shannon's older sister Holly had made birth announcements. They asked the nurse for a copy of Shannon's tiny footprints from her birth certificate, made lots of copies, and then glued a tiny footprint on the inside of each announcement. She and Holly had had so much fun making them. It was probably the first time Kaye had laughed since before Shannon's birth, and Kaye mailed the birth announcements on her way to the hospital the next morning. When Kaye arrived in the intensive care nursery, the nurse who was caring for Shannon told her that the ophthalmologist had stopped by to see Shannon and wanted to talk to her.

Shannon had retinopathy of prematurity (ROP), and the doctor wanted permission to do laser surgery on both of Shannon's eyes to stop the growth of the abnormal blood vessels. For the third time in Shannon's short life, she was put on an open, heated bed in the intensive care nursery and put under anesthesia for the procedure. Two weeks later, the disease was still progressing, and, once again, Shannon had surgery. This time the doctor performed cryotherapy, which involved inserting a tiny probe into Shannon's eyes to freeze the abnormal blood vessels. After the cryotherapy, Shannon's eye condition stabilized. It remained stable throughout the remainder of her stay in the neonatal intensive care unit, and for the 6 months afterward while Dr. Rubin was following Shannon's case.

Shannon's last visit to Dr. Rubin had been just a few weeks before Bruce was transferred and the Easons moved to the new house. "The ROP seems very stable now," Dr. Rubin had told Kaye. "It would be highly unlikely and extremely rare to see a progression of the disease so long after her due date. There's no need for her to continue to be checked as often." Kaye remembered how relieved she had felt at the time, but she realized now that she never should have let down her guard. It had made the news from Shannon's new ophthalmologist, Dr. Sharpe, that much more unbearable.

"The retinopathy of prematurity has now permanently damaged the retina of Shannon's right eye," Dr. Sharpe had informed Kaye last month. "Her left eye appears more normal, but it

86

is too soon to tell exactly how well the left eye will see. The wandering and erratic eye movements you have been seeing are symptoms of problems deep within the eye." Kaye nearly crumpled and fell to the floor right there in his office, but she held herself together until after the children had gone to bed that night. Then she cried as she had never cried before. Bruce's comforting arms were of little help against the pain Kaye had felt that night. The doctor's words echoed through her mind, along with the haunting images those words conjured up. Blind . . . partially sighted. . . visually impaired. . . . No! This couldn't be happening to Shannon. It wasn't fair! Hadn't they been through enough already? Why this? Why now? Why Shannon?

The following morning, Kaye called to schedule a vision assessment for Shannon. She had not wanted to make the call, but Dr. Sharpe recommended it, so she did it—for Shannon's sake. Virginia Cousins, a vision specialist, had come out to the house to see Shannon a week later. Virginia was pleasant enough and had given Kaye some helpful suggestions for working with Shannon, but her chirpy voice and "good news" approach irritated Kaye. Shannon's vision problem was *not* good news, and sugar-coating it wasn't going to make it go away. That night, Kaye cried again.

Kaye eventually forced herself to read a book about children who are blind or partially sighted, but her reading had gone slowly. She could only take in so much at a time, and she often had to put the book aside after reading just a few pages. The thought of Shannon not being able to see was almost too great a burden to bear. Kaye remembered the intimate hours she had spent looking at picture books with Holly when Holly was a baby. She also thought about the precious moments she now shared with 3-year-old Brett, looking at butterflies, birds, and assorted crawling insects. Only last week, she and Brett had run out in the backyard after a heavy rain and stared up in wonder at a rainbow that spanned the horizon. Would she be able to share these same things with Shannon? Would Shannon ever know the enchantment of a rainbow after a summer storm?

As always, Bruce was there for Kaye to help shoulder her pain. But this time Bruce didn't seem to understand why Kaye was feeling the way she was. "We've been through worse than this, Kaye," he had said. "The hard part is over. She's alive, and she's going to stay alive. We knew she might have problems after all of the eye surgery she went through. But we can cope with it." Kaye wasn't so sure that she could, and the difference in how she and Bruce felt about Shannon's problems created a distance between them that Kaye had never experienced before.

Bruce was right, the other part *had* been hard. Kaye remembered all too vividly the terror that had surrounded Shannon's early birth—the bleeding that wouldn't stop, being denied the home birth they had planned, coming home without a baby, and then watching helplessly as Shannon teetered on the fine line that separated life from death. For 5 long months, Kaye had lived with Holly and Brett in a single room at the Ronald McDonald House, apart from Bruce, who had made the 300-mile trek every Friday night to be with them. Kaye remembered the tears, the worry, and her endless prayers to let Shannon live. Yes, that part had been hard, but so was this. What made this part so hard was that it was different. This part was forever.

Kaye remembered what the doctors in the intensive care nursery had said the morning before she had boarded the small plane to go home with Shannon—at least home to the hospital in the small town where they had then lived. They had said that Shannon would need to be on oxygen for a year or so but that her lung tissue would regenerate as she grew bigger and that she would eventually outgrow her lung disease. They had said that by the time Shannon was 5 years old she should be caught up with other children in both size and development. Until then, Shannon would probably sit, crawl, and walk later than other children. And so, Kaye had told herself that she would eventually get the perfect, normal child she had imagined before Shannon's untimely birth if she just waited long enough.

But that wasn't true anymore. Although Shannon's scarred lungs would probably heal, nothing was going to restore her lost sight. Maybe Kaye didn't completely understand the degree of

Shannon's vision loss, but she did know that whatever had been lost wasn't going to come back. The damage had been done. Nothing was going to change that.

Because Dr. Rubin's predictions about Shannon's eyes had been wrong, Kaye also worried that it was possible that the other doctors' predictions about Shannon's development might be wrong, too. Kaye desperately wanted to believe that Shannon would catch up with typically developing children by the time she was 5 years old. But was she just setting herself up to be hurt again? After all, Shannon rarely tried to reach out for a toy, she wasn't babbling and cooing like other babies, she wasn't rolling over, and she could barely hold her head up by herself. Just how much of this could be blamed on Shannon's prematurity and the fact that she had been sick for so long? Then again, if Kaye didn't believe in her own daughter, who would?

On the days when Kaye worried about these things, she often thought about Sarintha and Ruth, two women whose babies had been in the intensive care nursery with Shannon. Their babies had also weighed under 2 pounds at birth, but they had been born at 28 and 29 weeks' gestation, and they had gone home long before Shannon—and without oxygen. By the time Shannon went home, Sarintha's and Ruth's babies were already sitting up and crawling. Kaye had kept in touch with them for awhile, but the number of contacts dwindled rapidly as the differences between Sarintha's and Ruth's babies and Shannon became more apparent.

Shortly after the Easons received Dr. Sharpe's news, Shannon's feeding problems escalated. She started fighting the gavage feeding more and more, and her vomiting increased to the point where she was, once again, losing weight. The doctor determined that Shannon had gastroesophogeal reflux and suggested a gastrostomy so that Shannon could be fed by a pump at night while she slept. The idea of freeing Shannon from the torture of the night-time gavage feedings was appealing, as was the previously unimagined idea that Kaye might get more than 3 hours of sleep at a time. Besides, Shannon wasn't making any progress toward being able to drink from a bottle. It still took her more than half an hour to drink 2 ounces. Attempts to feed Shannon solid foods were no more promising; she gagged and spit out the baby cereal and strained fruits each time they were offered. Although Kaye and Bruce agreed to the gastrostomy, Kaye felt as if she was being disloyal to Shannon, like she was giving up on her.

Kaye remembered Holly's and Brett's reactions when she had told them that Shannon would be going into the hospital for a few days to have the gastrostomy done. Holly was appalled at the idea that Shannon would be fed that way, and she cried. It was the first time that Holly had shown any strong emotions about what was happening to her little sister. Brett, however, thought it was the best thing he had ever heard of. He asked question after question about the "tummy plug" that Shannon was going to have put in. He was a little concerned, however, that Shannon might not be able to have trick-or-treat candy on Halloween; but he quickly decided that if she couldn't have the candy, he would eat some of it for her and save the rest so she could have it when she was bigger like he was.

Shannon's first birthday was 4 days before her scheduled gastrostomy, and Bruce had thought that he and Kaye should have a small party for her. They would invite Kaye's parents, his mother, and his brother and sister-in-law and their two children. Kaye had suggested to Bruce that they wait and celebrate on Shannon's due date, but he wouldn't hear of it. "Her birthday is the day she was born," he had said firmly. "Are we still going to be talking about her *gestational age* when she's in college?" Seeing the hurt look on Kaye's face, Bruce pulled her close and embraced her. "I'm sorry," he said. "I just think she's been robbed of enough as it is. I don't want to take away her birthday, too. Maybe she is behind, but she has still been alive for a year, and I think we should celebrate." Bruce looked into Kaye's eyes and gave her a boyish grin. "Can we compromise and celebrate both dates?" he asked. Shannon had her party.

Kaye had not wanted to tell Shannon's grandparents and the rest of the family about Shannon's upcoming surgery. It had been hard enough when they had had to tell them the bad news about her eyes only a few weeks earlier. Bruce, however, thought that the family should be told, that they had a right to know. After all, hadn't he and Kaye involved them in everything concerning Shannon from the time she was born? Why should they start keeping secrets from them now? Kaye knew he was right, and after the last remnants of the birthday party had been cleared away and the adults had settled down in the living room for coffee, they broke the news about Shannon's gastrostomy. Kaye couldn't hold back her tears as she told Shannon's grandparents what the procedure involved and why it had to be done.

Kaye had convinced Bruce not to tell anyone else about Shannon's impending surgery yet, not even their friends at church. Kaye had grown tired of seeing the look of pity in people's eyes every time she told them, yet again, about something else that was wrong with Shannon. Others would view the gastrostomy as a setback, as a sign that Shannon was going downhill. Kaye knew she wasn't, but *they* would see it that way. They wouldn't understand.

Kaye's thoughts once again focused on Beth Mason's approaching visit. What would she have to say today? Would she tell them that something else was wrong with Shannon? Why else would Virginia Cousins have recommended that Kaye call the early intervention program and have someone come out to see Shannon? Although she had said only that Shannon might benefit from the occupational therapy the early intervention program offered, was it possible that Virginia Cousins had noticed something else about Shannon that she couldn't bring herself to tell Kaye?

And what if this Beth Mason *did* tell Kaye there was something else wrong with Shannon? She would probably suggest activities or therapy for Kaye to do with Shannon. Of course, Kaye would do whatever Beth suggested; she would do anything to help her daughter. But how? Kaye already found it difficult to meet the needs of her other two children because she was spending so much time caring for Shannon.

As it was, Holly was behind in her school work. Kaye had continued Holly's home schooling while Shannon was in the hospital and they were living at the Ronald McDonald House, but they had fallen behind in the curriculum. After Shannon came home, Kaye and Bruce had discussed the possibility of sending Holly to public school, but they had decided against it. The schools in the rural area where they now lived weren't very good, and Kaye enjoyed home schooling Holly. It gave her an opportunity to put her degree in education to good use. In fact, Kaye looked forward to home schooling Brett and Shannon, too. Kaye was a little concerned, however, about Holly's social life. Holly was 11 years old, an age when close friendships were so important. Holly had made a few friends while playing soccer, and she occasionally invited them over to the house; but, Kaye wondered whether this was enough. She knew she would be able to do so much more for Holly if Shannon didn't require so much time and if Shannon were more portable.

Then there was Brett. What a little trooper he had been over the past year! When Kaye first found out she was pregnant with Shannon, she and Bruce had talked about how Brett might react to a new baby in the house. They had discussed ways to make the transition easier for Brett and to ensure that he still received his fair share of attention. Little did they know just how much Brett's world would be turned upside down when Shannon was born. But, despite the disruption and confusion, Brett remained a happy and cooperative toddler. Everyone always commented on how well he had handled the situation. Then one day when Kaye was in the middle of a lengthy bottle feeding with Shannon, Brett had leaned on the arm of the rocking chair and quietly watched Shannon drink. After a minute or two, he looked up at Kaye and announced, "I'll be glad when she grows up and *I'm* the baby." Brett's words broke Kaye's heart. She realized then that her sweet Brett had been far more patient in waiting for Shannon to get better than all the rest of them put together.

When the Easons had lived at the old house, Bruce's mother and Kaye's parents had been a big help in picking up the slack. Bruce's mother, a widow for 9 years, had lived nearby and had stopped by the house often to bring over a casserole or a pie, spend some time playing with Brett, or take the children out for an ice cream cone or other special treat. She had also been the person who Bruce and Kaye counted on to stay with Holly and Brett when they had to be somewhere else with Shannon. Kaye's mom and dad had lived a little farther away, but they, too, had come for occasional weekend visits to spoil the kids and to take care of Kaye. Kaye had loved it when they would come to visit; she didn't have to wash a single dish from the moment they arrived until the time they left.

Now that Kaye and Bruce had moved, the children's grandparents couldn't be around as much. The Easons' new house was at least a full day's drive away for both Bruce's mother and Kaye's parents. What Kaye missed most about their visits was the special attention that Holly and Brett had always received from their grandparents—the attention that Kaye herself was often too busy or too tired to give. Kaye also missed the close friendships and support she and Bruce had had through their old church. They had joined a new church when they moved, and upon learning about Shannon, several members of the congregation had offered a helping hand and their friendship. But it wasn't the same as before. These relationships were still too new. The only other assistance the Easons received was when they occasionally employed a respite nurse to care for Shannon while Kaye went to the grocery store or while she and Bruce went to a church function. Respite nursing, however, was expensive, and they had to be careful how much they used it or Bruce's insurance wouldn't cover the costs.

Rather than wait idly for Beth Mason to arrive, Kaye started the soup stock for dinner. If she kept busy, maybe she wouldn't get so anxious. As she diced the vegetables for the stock, Kaye looked over her shoulder at Brett who was busy at the kitchen table. With his tongue sticking out of the corner of his mouth, Brett was completely absorbed in drawing a big, yellow sun at the top of his picture. Kaye then peered around the corner of the table to see what Shannon was doing. Shannon's head was turned toward the window, and the bright sun shone in upon her face. Kaye couldn't tell if she was awake or asleep.

Looking at Shannon, Kaye was reminded of the little girl that she had seen at the meeting on Monday evening. The nurse at Shannon's new pediatrician's office had told Kaye about a support group for parents of premature babies that met on the first Monday night of each month. Kaye had told Bruce about it, and he offered to stay home with the children so she could go. Halfway through the meeting there had been a refreshment break, and Kaye had walked out to the lobby to be by herself for a minute or two. That was where she met the 4-year-old girl and her mother. The little girl had blond hair, wore glasses, and her eyes were a bit crossed. She scooted around the carpeted lobby on plastic roller skates while her mother talked to Kaye. Kaye was surprised to find out that the child had been born at almost the same gestational age and birth weight as Shannon. The mother said that her daughter had been very late in doing everything; including not learning to walk until she was 2 years old. But, as Kaye could see for herself, the little girl was doing fine now. After all the doubts that Kaye had experienced over the past month, it was encouraging to meet this child and her mother.

Kaye needed encouragement. She needed to believe that Shannon would thrive, that all her efforts and prayers had not been in vain. Kaye had already lost one child—Shannon's twin, whom Kaye had miscarried. Of course, Kaye hadn't known she had been carrying twins until after the bleeding had started and the doctor did a sonogram. Kaye still recalled the mixture of emotions she had experienced back then. Her heart had leapt with joy when the doctor told her she was still pregnant and she saw the movement of their tiny baby on the computer screen. But there was also a touch of sadness when the doctor then pointed out the tiny, empty sac that had once enveloped the child of theirs whom they would never know.

More than anything else, Kaye needed some answers. What would Shannon be like when she was 3 years old, 6 years old, or when she was Holly's age? How would her vision impairment affect her life? Could Shannon ever really be like the little girl with glasses who scooted around on her roller skates? Just how long must Kaye wait for answers? How long would it be before she would know what the future held in store for her baby girl?